Sing the Journey

HYMNAL: A WORSHIP BOOK
SUPPLEMENT I

Sing the Journey
Hymnal: A Worship Book—Supplement 1

Copyright © 2005 by Faith & Life Resources, a division of Mennonite Publishing Network, Scottdale, Pa. 15683

International Standard Book Number: 0-8361-9300-8

Music engraving by James E. Clemens
Cover design by Gwen Stamm

Printed in Canada by Friesens, Altona, Manitoba

Cover symbol—The lamb in the midst of briars is a traditional Anabaptist symbol. It illustrates the suffering Lamb of God, who calls the faithful to obedient service.

10 09 08 07 06 05   10 9 8 7 6 5 4 3

To order or request information, please call 1 800 245-7894.
www.mph.org

Faith & Life Resources
A division of Mennonite Publishing Network
Mennonite Church USA and
Mennonite Church Canada

INTRODUCTION

Our singing reveals much about who we have been and who we are as Anabaptists ...
—introduction of *Hymnal: A Worship Book*

The volume that you hold in your hands is a continuation of the work of *Hymnal: A Worship Book*. When it appeared in 1992, *Hymnal*'s contents unleashed a significant flood of creative activity in Mennonite churches, in the form of new tunes and texts. The initial response of the publishers was to begin the *Hymnal Subscription Service* (1997-2003), which made available to congregations 270 new hymns and other worship resources.

Sing the Journey, the second phase of response, is drawn from materials introduced in the *Subscription Service* and from other new resources not readily available. *Sing the Journey* is modeled on *Hymnal: A Worship Book*. Its table of contents uses the same outline. It is intended as a prayer book that contains rich musical and textual color. It is attentive to the gifts of the worldwide church and to the variety of religious experience within our denomination. Finally, it brings back some well-loved and often-missed hymns, while also offering materials that will lure congregations into new song.

Sing the Journey is the first of a two-part *Hymnal* supplement, divided along the two halves of the Christian calendar. This volume explores the life of the Church and its mission in the world, corresponding to the season between Pentecost and Advent. It assumes that the work of the Holy Spirit continues in the present, and that the life of the Church, though changing, is not ever fully known or ever entirely complete. The second volume will focus on the life of Jesus, corresponding to the church year from Advent through Easter.

It is with confidence that those who collected and chose materials, along with those who shepherded the publishing process, offer this volume to the glory of God, whose praise is sung by God's people throughout time and eternity, and in all places. We hope that the community of faith is widened through the use of this book, and that we all will be moved to sing more frequently and in more places. This is the church's calling: to worship, to reach out, to find common and welcome space—even when fear and paralyzing tensions threaten to keep us apart from one another and from God.

Toward a goal of giving voice to the church as it emerges in the next generation of its life, we have given our time, our imagination, and our work. May God's blessings rest on this book, and upon and within all who use it.

—Ken Nafziger

Members of the *Hymnal* supplement committee:
Randall Spaulding, Marlene Kropf, Kenneth J. Nafziger, Jeff Enns, James E. Clemens, Carmen Horst, Marilyn Houser Hamm

TABLE OF CONTENTS

We sing to you, O God

DARWALL'S 148th 66. 66. 88

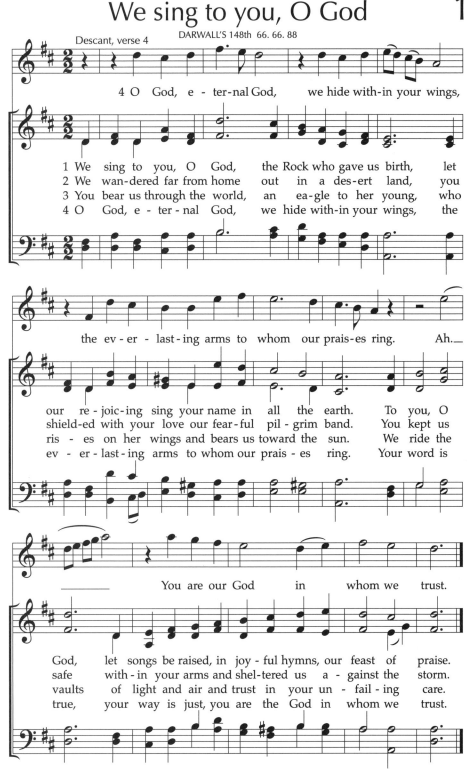

Descant, verse 4

4 O   God, e - ter-nal God,   we hide with-in your wings,

1 We   sing to you, O   God,   the Rock who gave us birth,   let
2 We   wan-dered far from home   out   in a des-ert land,   you
3 You   bear us through the world,   an   ea-gle to her young,   who
4 O   God, e - ter - nal God,   we hide with-in your wings,   the

the ev - er - last-ing arms to whom our prais-es ring.   Ah.__

our re - joic-ing sing your name in   all   the earth.   To you, O
shield-ed with your love our fear-ful   pil - grim band.   You kept us
ris - es on her wings and bears us toward the   sun.   We ride the
ev - er - last-ing arms to whom our prais - es   ring.   Your word is

You are our God   in   whom we   trust.

God,   let songs be raised, in joy - ful hymns, our feast of   praise.
safe   with - in your arms and shel-tered us   a - gainst the   storm.
vaults   of light and air and trust in   your un - fail - ing   care.
true,   your way is just, you are the   God in   whom we   trust.

Text: Gracia Grindal, based on Deuteronomy 32:11, 18; 33:27; Psalms 57:1; 66:2; 96:1-2
Music: John Darwall, *New Universal Psalmodist*, 1770; descant by Charles H. Webb, alt.
Descant copyright © 1980 Harold Flammer, Inc.

2 Hamba nathi (Come, walk with us)

Irregular

Text: South African traditional; translated by Gerhard Cartford
Copyright © Lutheran World Foundation
Music: South African traditional; arranged by Anders Nyberg
Copyright © 1984 Utryck; admin. Walton Music Corp. Used by permission.

mku - lu - lu we - thu,
The jour-ney is long.

lu - lu,   mku-lu - lu,   mku - lu - lu we - thu,   mku -
jour-ney,   the jour-ney,   the jour-ney is long.   The

mku - lu - lu we-thu,
The jour-ney is long.

lu - lu, mku-lu-lu, mku - lu-lu we-thu,   mku - lu - lu we-thu.
jour-ney, the jour-ney, the jour-ney is long.   The jour-ney is long.

2 Share our burden, and join in the song
3 Come, uplift us and bring us new life
4 Give us peace when the journey is done

3 Jesus calls us here to meet him

87. 87D

Text: John L. Bell and Graham Maule
Music: Lewis folk melody; arranged by John L. Bell
Text and Music copyright © WGRG The Iona Community (Scotland).
Used by permission of GIA Publications, Inc., exclusive agent.

You've got a place

Irregular

1 You've got a place at the wel - come ta - ble,
2 We're goin' to feast on— milk and hon - ey,
3 We'll give— thanks at the wel - come ta - ble,
4 We'll come— home to the wel - come ta - ble,

you've got a place at the wel - come ta - ble, some of these
we're goin' to feast on— milk and hon - ey, some of these
we'll give— thanks at the wel - come ta - ble, some of these
we'll come— home to the wel - come ta - ble, some of these

days. Hal - le - lu - jah! You've got a
days. Hal - le - lu - jah! We're goin' to
days. Hal - le - lu - jah! We'll give—
days. Hal - le - lu - jah! We'll come—

place at the wel - come ta - ble, you've got a
feast on— milk and hon - ey, we're goin' to
thanks at the wel - come ta - ble, we'll give—
home to the wel - come ta - ble, we'll come—

place at the wel - come ta - ble, some of these days.
feast on— milk and hon - ey, some of these days.
thanks at the wel - come ta - ble, some of these days.
home to the wel - come ta - ble, some of these days.

Text: traditional spiritual
Music: traditional spiritual

5 Come and be light for our eyes

10 9. 10 9 with refrain

Text: David Haas
Music: David Haas

bod - y   and blood,   new   life in our midst!
Your name now names   us   peo - ple of God!
sing - ing, pro - claim   - ing   Je - sus is Lord!

Death is   no lon - ger,   life is the fu - ture;
Filled with your vi - sion,   peo - ple of mis - sion,
Teach us   to speak,   and   help us to lis - ten

Je - sus, Mes - si - ah,   name of   all names!
heal - ing, for - giv - ing; light for   the world!
for when your truth   and   our dreams em - brace!

6

Jesu tawa pano
(Jesus, we are here)

JESU TAWA PANO Irregular

Shona: Je - su   ta - wa   pa - no;   Je - su
English: Je - sus, we   are   here;____   Je - sus,
German: Je - sus, wir   sind   hier;____   Je - sus,
French: Je - sus, nous   sommes   i - ci;   Je - sus,
Spanish: Je - sús   a - quí es - ta - mos;   Je - sús

ta - wa   pa - no;   Je - su   ta - wa   pa - no;
we   are   here;____   Je - sus, we   are   here;____
wir   sind   hier;____   Je - sus, wir   sind   hier;____
nous sommes   i - ci;   Je - sus, nous sommes   i - ci;
a - quí es - ta - mos;   Je - sús   a - quí es - ta - mos;

Leader (omit last time):
Ma - mbo Je - su.
Wel - come, Je - sus.
Komm jetzt, Je - sus.
Ve - nez, Jé - sus.
Ven,   Je - sús.____

ta - wa   pa - no,   mu   zi - ta re - nyu.
we   are   here_____   for_____   you.
wir   sind   hier_____   für_____   dich.
nous sommes   i - ci_____   pour_____   toi.
a - quí es - ta - mos_____   pa - ra   ti.

Other verses may be sung replacing Jesu/Jesus with Savior, Master, Spirit,...

Text: Patrick Matsikenyiri, Zimbabwe
Music: Patrick Matsikenyiri, Zimbabwe

Silently, peacefully

WE WILL REST IN YOU* Irregular with refrain

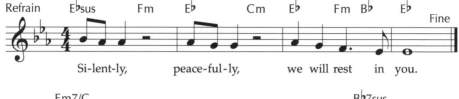

Si-lent-ly, peace-ful-ly, we will rest in you.

1 O come, bless the Lord, all you who
2 Lift up your hands to the
3 Glory to the Father, and

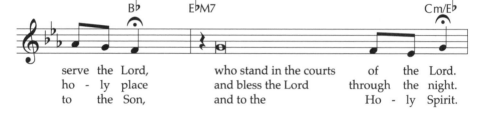

serve the Lord, who stand in the courts of the Lord.
ho - ly place and bless the Lord through the night.
to the Son, and to the Ho - ly Spirit.

O come, bless the Lord, all you who serve the Lord,
— May the Lord bless you from Zion,
As al - ways be - fore, so now and ev - er - more.

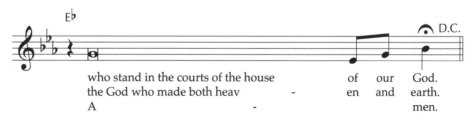

who stand in the courts of the house of our God.
the God who made both heav - en and earth.
A - men.

*Original title

Text: Mike Hay, based on Psalm 134
Music: Mike Hay

8 Somos pueblo que camina (We are people on a journey)

87 with refrain

1 So - mos pue-blo que ca - mi - na   por la sen-da del do - lor.
2 Los hu-mil-des y los po - bres   in - vi - ta-dos son de   Dios.
1 We are peo-ple on a jour-ney;   pain is with us all the   way.
2 God has sent the in - vi - ta - tion   to the hum-ble and the   poor.

Refrain

A - cu-da-mos ju - bi - lo-sos   a la san-ta co - mu-nión.
Joy-ful-ly we come to-geth-er   at the ho-ly feast   of God.

Text: La Misa Popular Nicaragüense (20th c.); tr. Carolyn Jennings, "Somos pueblo que camina (We Are People on a Journey),"
  from *The New Century Hymnal* (Cleveland: The Pilgrim Press, 1981), 340.
  Translation copyright © 1993 The Pilgrim Press. Used by permission.
Music: La Misa Popular Nicaragüense (20th c.)

9 Come, now is the time to worship

Irregular

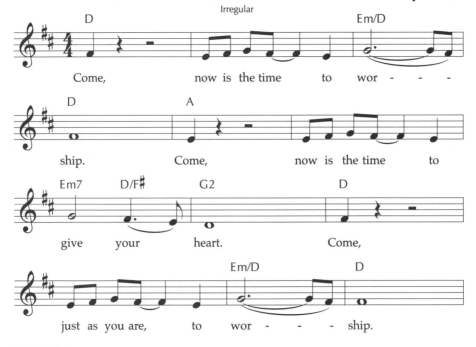

Come,   now is the time   to   wor - - -

ship.   Come,   now is the time   to

give   your   heart.   Come,

just as you are,   to   wor - - - - ship.

Text: Brian Doerksen
Music: Brian Doerksen
  Text and Music copyright © 1998 Vineyard Songs (UK/Eire);
  admin. in North America by Music Services o/b/o Vineyard Music Global Inc. (PRS)

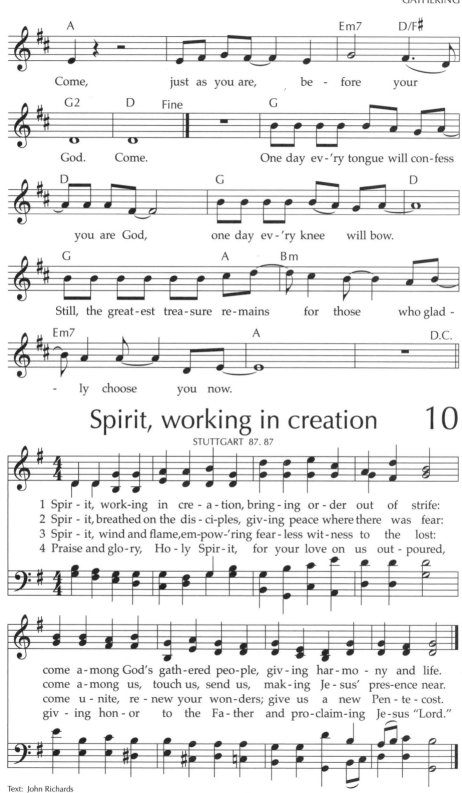

Come, just as you are, be - fore your

God. Come. One day ev-'ry tongue will con-fess

you are God, one day ev-'ry knee will bow.

Still, the great-est trea-sure re-mains for those who glad -

- ly choose you now.

Spirit, working in creation 10

STUTTGART 87. 87

1 Spir - it, work-ing in cre - a - tion, bring-ing or - der out of strife:
2 Spir - it, breathed on the dis - ci-ples, giv-ing peace where there was fear:
3 Spir - it, wind and flame, em-pow-'ring fear - less wit-ness to the lost:
4 Praise and glo-ry, Ho - ly Spir-it, for your love on us out - poured,

come a-mong God's gath-ered peo-ple, giv-ing har-mo - ny and life.
come a-mong us, touch us, send us, mak-ing Je - sus' pres-ence near.
come u - nite, re - new your won-ders; give us a new Pen - te - cost.
giv - ing hon - or to the Fa - ther and pro-claim-ing Je - sus "Lord."

Text: John Richards
Copyright © John Richards
Music: attributed to C. F. Witt, *Psalmodia Sacra,* 1715; adapted by Henry J. Gauntlett, 1861

11 Praise, praise, praise the Lord!

CAMEROON PRAISE 59. 59. 99. 99

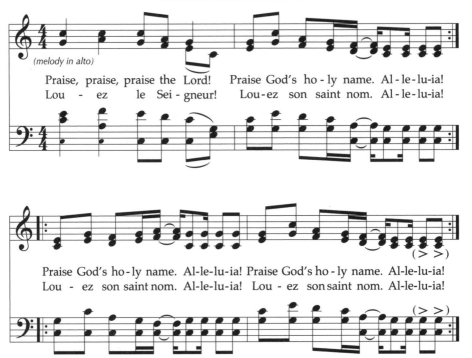

(melody in alto)

Praise, praise, praise the Lord! Praise God's ho - ly name. Al - le - lu - ia!
Lou - ez le Sei - gneur! Lou - ez son saint nom. Al - le - lu - ia!

Praise God's ho - ly name. Al - le - lu - ia! Praise God's ho - ly name. Al - le - lu - ia!
Lou - ez son saint nom. Al - le - lu - ia! Lou - ez son saint nom. Al - le - lu - ia!

Text: Cameroon traditional; collected by Elaine Hanson
Music: Cameroon processional; arr. Ralph M. Johnson

Cantai ao Senhor
(O sing to the Lord)

12

56.56.56.55

1 Can - tai ao Se - nhor um
1 O sing to the Lord, O

cân - ti - co no - vo, can - tai ao Se - nhor um
sing God a new song. O sing to the Lord, O

cân - ti - co no - vo, can - tai ao Se - nhor um
sing God a new song. O sing to the Lord, O

cân - ti - co no - vo, can - tai ao Se - nhor, can -
sing God a new song. O sing to the Lord, O

tai ao Se - nhor.
sing to the Lord.

PORTUGUESE

2 Porque ele fez, ele faz maravilhas, (3x)
cantai ao Senhor, cantai ao Senhor!

3 Cantai ao Senhor, bendizei o seu nome, (3x)
cantai ao Senhor, cantai ao Senhor!

4 É ele quem dá o Espírito Santo, (3x)
cantai ao Senhor, cantai ao Senhor!

5 Jesus é o Senhor! Amém, aleluia! (3x)
cantai ao Senhor, cantai ao Senhor!

ENGLISH

2 By his holy power the Lord has done wonders. (3x)
O sing to the Lord, O sing to the Lord.

3 So dance for the Lord and blow all the trumpets. (3x)
O sing to the Lord, O sing to the Lord.

4 O shout to the Lord, who gave us the Spirit. (3x)
O sing to the Lord, O sing to the Lord.

5 For Jesus is Lord! Amen! Alleluia! (3x)
O sing to the Lord, O sing to the Lord.

Text: Brazilian traditional, based on Psalm 98
Music: Brazilian traditional

13 My soul is filled with joy

WILD MOUNTAIN THYME Irregular with refrain

1 My___ soul is filled with joy as I
2 I am low-ly as a child, but I
3 I pro-claim the pow'r of God: you do
4 To the hun-gry you give food, send the
5 In your love you now ful - fill what you

1 sing to God my sav - ior: you have looked up-on your
2 know from this day for-ward that my name will be re-
3 mar - vels for your ser-vants; though you scat - ter the proud
4 rich a - way___ emp - ty. In your mer - cy you are
5 prom - ised to your peo-ple. I will praise you, Lord, my

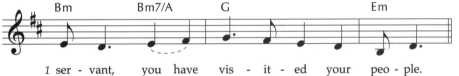

1 ser - vant, you have vis - it - ed your peo - ple.
2 mem-bered, for___ all will call me bless - ed.
3 heart - ed and de - stroy the might of princ - es.
4 mind - ful of the peo - ple you have cho - sen.
5 sav - ior, ev - er - last - ing is your mer - cy.

Refrain

Soprano (Melody)

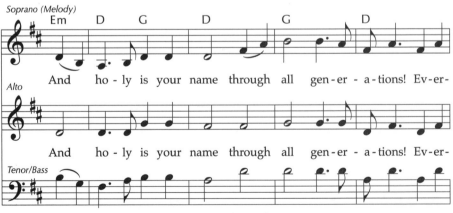

Alto

And ho - ly is your name through all gen - er - a - tions! Ev-er-

And ho - ly is your name through all gen - er - a - tions! Ev-er-

Tenor/Bass

And ho - ly is your name through all gen - er - a - tions! Ev-er-

Text: David Haas, based on Luke 1:46-55
Music: Irish traditional, arranged by David Haas
Text and Music copyright © 1989 G.I.A. Publications, Inc.

last - ing is your mer-cy to the peo - ple you have cho-sen, and

last - ing is your mer-cy to the peo - ple you have cho-sen, and

last - ing is your mer-cy to the peo - ple you have cho-sen, and

ho - ly is your name.

ho - ly is your name.

ho - ly is your name.

14 Lord Jesus, you shall be my song

LES PETITES SOEURS 12 14. 12 12

1 Lord Je-sus, you shall be my song as I jour-ney; I'll
2 Lord Je-sus, I'll praise you as long as I jour-ney. May
1 Jé-sus, je vou-drais te chan-ter sur ma rou-te; Jé-
2 Jé-sus, je vou-drais te lou-er sur ma rou-te; Jé-

tell ev-'ry-bod-y a-bout you wher-ev-er I go:
all of my joy be a faith-ful re-flec-tion of you.
sus, je vou-drais t'an-non-cer à mes voi-sins par-tout,
sus, je vou-drais que ma voix soit l'é-cho de ta joie,

you a-lone are our life and our peace and our love. Lord
May the earth and the sea and the sky join my song. Lord
car toi seul es la vie et la paix et l'a-mour: Jé-
et que chan-te la terre et que chan-te le ciel; Jé-

Je-sus, you shall be my song as I jour-ney.
Je-sus, I'll praise you as long as I jour-ney.
sus, je vou-drais te chan-ter sur ma rou-te.
sus, je vou-drais te lou-er sur ma rou-te.

ENGLISH

3 As long as I live, Jesus, make me your servant
   to carry your cross and to share all your burdens
     and tears.
   For you saved me by giving your body and blood.
   As long as I live, Jesus, make me your servant.

4 I fear in the dark and the doubt of my journey;
   but courage will come with the sound of your steps
     by my side.
   And with all of the family you saved by your love,
   we'll sing to your dawn at the end of our journey.

FRENCH

3 Jésus, je voudrais te servir sur ma route,
   Jésus, je voudrais partager les soufrances de
     ta croix,
   car tu livres pour moi et ton corps et ton sang;
   Jésus, je voudrais te servir sur ma route.

4 Jésus, je voudrais tour au long de ma route,
   entendre tes pas résonner dans le nuit près
     de moi,
   jusqu'à l'aube du jour où ton peuple sauvé,
   Jésus, chantera ton retour sur ma route.

Santo (Holy) 15

ARGENTINA 67. 95

Text: Variation on traditional liturgical text
Music: unknown; arranged by The Iona Community, based on two-part version as taught by Pablo Sosa
    Arrangement copyright © 1990 WGRG The Iona Community (Scotland).
    Used by permission of G.I.A. Publications, Inc., exclusive agent.

16 Praise with joy the world's Creator

BENEDIC ANIMA 87.87.87

1 Praise with joy the world's Cre - a - tor, God of jus-tice,
2 Praise to Christ who feeds the hun - gry, frees the cap-tive,
3 Praise the Spir - it sent a - mong us, lib - er - at-ing
4 Praise the Mak - er, Christ, and Spir - it, one God in com-

love, and peace, source and end of hu - man knowl-edge,
finds the lost, heals the sick, up - sets re - li - gion,
truth from pride, forg - ing bonds where race or gen - der,
mu - ni - ty, call - ing Chris - tians to em - bod - y

God whose grace shall nev - er cease. Cel - e - brate the
fear - less both of fate and cost. Cel - e - brate Christ's
age or na - tion dare di - vide. Cel - e - brate the
one - ness and di - ver - si - ty. This the world shall

Mak - er's glo - ry, power to res - cue and re - lease.
con - stant pres-ence: friend and strang - er, guest and host.
Spir - it's trea-sure: fool - ish - ness none dare de - ride.
see re - flect - ed: God is One and One in Three.

Text: The Iona Community, 1985, alt.
Copyright © 1987 WGRG The Iona Community (Scotland). Used by permission of G.I.A. Publications, Inc., exclusive agent.
Music: John Goss, *The Supplemental Hymn and Tune Book*, 1869

Halle, halle, hallelujah!

Text: Caribbean traditional
Music: Caribbean traditional; arranged by John L. Bell
Arrangement copyright © 1990 WGRG The Iona Community (Scotland).
Used by permission of GIA Publications, Inc., exclusive agent.

18 Over my head

OVER MY HEAD 77. 77. 77. 7 with refrain

Refrain

O-ver my head, I hear mu-sic in the air; o-ver my head,

I hear mu - sic in the air; o-ver my head,

I hear mu-sic in the air; there must be a God some-

Solo

1 Oh, when the world is si - lent,
2 And when I'm feel - ing lone - ly,
3 Now when I think on Je - sus,

Fine

where. (Hum) I hear

Text: African-American traditional
Music: African-American traditional; arranged by The Iona Community
Text and Arrangement copyright © 1998 WGRG The Iona Community (Scotland).
Used by permission of G.I.A. Publications, Inc., exclusive agent.

19 I will call upon the Lord

Irregular

I will call up-on the Lord, who is wor-thy to be
I will call up-on the Lord,

praised. So shall I be saved from my en-e-mies.
who is wor-thy to be praised. So shall I be

The Lord liv-eth, and bless-ed be the Rock;
saved from my en-e-mies.

and let the God of my sal-va - tion be ex - al - ted. The

Lord liv-eth, and bless-ed be the Rock; and let the God

Text: Michael O'Shields, based on Psalm 18:2 and 2 Samuel 22:47
Music: Michael O'Shields; arr. Joseph Joubert
Text and Music copyright © 1981 Sound III
Arrangement copyright © 2000 G.I.A. Publications, Inc.

of my sal-va - tion be ex - al - ted.

Agios o Theos

20

RUSSIA 66. 76

A - gi-os o The-os, a - gi-os is - chi-ros,

a - gi-os a - tha-na - tos, e - le - i - son i - mas.*

*Translation: Holy God, holy and mighty, holy and immortal, have mercy on us.

Pronunciation: Ah-ghee-awss aw Theh-awss, ah-ghee-awss ees-hee-rawss,
ah-ghee-awss ah-thah-nah-tawss, eh-leh-ee-sawn ee-mahss.

Text: traditional
Music: Russian Orthodox Liturgy

21 Lamb of God

AGNUS DEI (ST. BRIDE SETTING)* Irregular

*Original title

Text: traditional liturgical
Music: The Iona Community
    Text and Music copyright © 2001 WGRG The Iona Community (Scotland).
    Used by permission of G.I.A. Publications, Inc., exclusive agent.

By the waters of Babylon

22

JAMAICAN PSALM 137 Irregular

Text: Jamaican traditional
Music: Jamaican traditional

23 Slowly turning, ever turning

COLUMCILLE (DOMHNACH TRIONOIDE) 87. 87D

Unison

1 Slow-ly turn-ing, ev-er turn-ing from our love-less-ness like ice,
2 Slow-ly turn-ing, ev-er turn-ing from our e - go-cen-tered gaze,
3 Slow-ly turn-ing, ev-er turn-ing from our fear of death and loss,

from our un-for-giv-ing spir - it, from the grip of en-vy's vise,
from our self - en-clos-ing cir - cle, from our nar - row, pet-ty ways,
from our ter - ror of the dark-ness, from our scorn-ing of the cross,

slow-ly turn-ing, ev-er turn - ing toward the lav - ish life of spring,
slow-ly turn-ing, ev-er turn - ing toward the for - eign - er as friend,
slow-ly turn-ing, ev-er turn - ing toward the true and faith-ful one,

toward the word of warmth and par-don, toward the mer - cy wel-com-ing!
toward the cit - y with-out ghet-to, toward the great-ness with-out end!
toward the light of day-break dawn-ing, toward the phoe - nix-ris-en sun!

Creation is a song

CREATION IS A SONG 76. 66 with chorus

Chorus

Cre - a - tion is a song, a song that we can see, a sa - cred gift from God, let's join the har - mo - ny.

Fine

1 The roll - ing of the o - ceans, the bub - bling of a spring,
2 Danc - ing prair - ie mead - ow, fruit sway - ing on the vine,
3 Ma - jes - tic sleep - ing moun - tain, for - est green and deep,
4 Ev - ery glow - ing sun - set, ev - ery out-stretched leaf is

D.C.

night sky filled with jew - els, a flock of beat - ing wings.
boil - ing storm clouds ris - ing, light - ning 'cross the sky.
ev - ery liv - ing crea - ture in our care to keep.
wit - ness to the glo - ry of the One who sits as Chief.

Alternate Chorus (Cheyenne)

Hoe i i ni mi yo niv, Ni wo da no ni,

Ma hay yo - o, Ni mi da no ni.

Pronunciation: O is long, as in "ocean." I is short, as in "gift."

Text: Doug Krehbiel and Jude Krehbiel, based on Psalm 19
Music: Doug Krehbiel and Jude Krehbiel

Copyright © 2003 Doug Krehbiel and Jude Krehbiel. Inspired by writings of Lawrence Hart, Cheyenne Christian Songs "given" to Maude Fighting Bear, and *Cheyenne Spiritual Songs,* tr. Lenora Hart Holliman

25 When long before time

11 11. 11 11

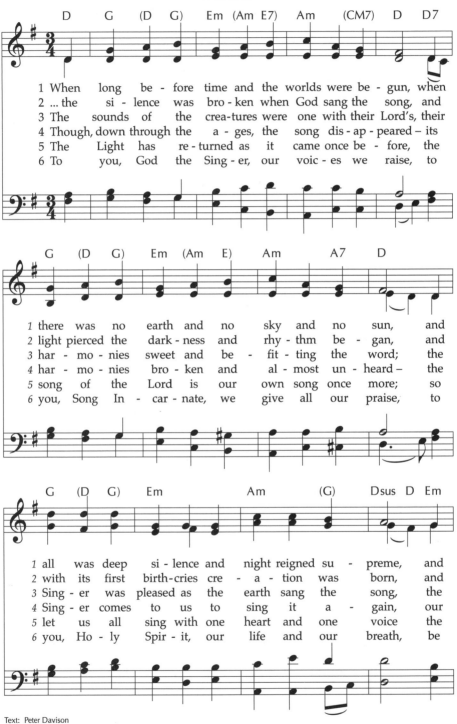

1 When long be - fore time and the worlds were be - gun, when
2 ... the si - lence was bro - ken when God sang the song, and
3 The sounds of the crea-tures were one with their Lord's, their
4 Though, down through the a - ges, the song dis - ap - peared – its
5 The Light has re - turned as it came once be - fore, the
6 To you, God the Sing - er, our voic - es we raise, to

1 there was no earth and no sky and no sun, and
2 light pierced the dark - ness and rhy - thm be - gan, and
3 har - mo - nies sweet and be - fit - ting the word; the
4 har - mo - nies bro - ken and al - most un - heard – the
5 song of the Lord is our own song once more; so
6 you, Song In - car - nate, we give all our praise, to

1 all was deep si - lence and night reigned su - preme, and
2 with its first birth-cries cre - a - tion was born, and
3 Sing - er was pleased as the earth sang the song, the
4 Sing - er comes to us to sing it a - gain, our
5 let us all sing with one heart and one voice the
6 you, Ho - ly Spir - it, our life and our breath, be

Text: Peter Davison
Music: Peter Davison; arr. George Black
Text and Music copyright © 1981 Peter W. A. Davison
Arrangement copyright © 1981 George Black

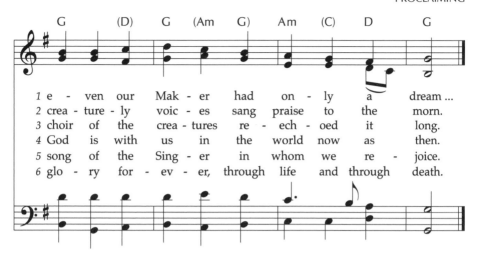

G   (D)   G   (Am   G)   Am   (C)   D   G

1 e - ven our Mak - er had on - ly a dream ...
2 crea - ture - ly voic - es sang praise to the morn.
3 choir of the crea - tures re - ech - oed it long.
4 God is with us in the world now as then.
5 song of the Sing - er in whom we re - joice.
6 glo - ry for - ev - er, through life and through death.

God is our refuge and strength 26

GOD OUR REFUGE* Irregular

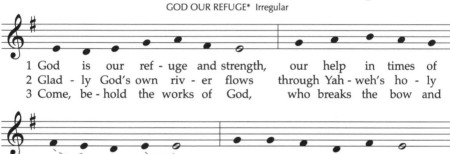

1 God is our ref - uge and strength, our help in times of
2 Glad - ly God's own riv - er flows through Yah - weh's ho - ly
3 Come, be - hold the works of God, who breaks the bow and

ter - ror and trou - ble. There - fore we shall not fear,
hab - i - ta - tion. It shall nev - er be moved,
shat - ters the spear,___ and brings us peace on earth.

though the earth shall change, though the moun - tains shall shake
though the na - tions fall, though the king - doms shall end;
Now, be still and know, know that Yah - weh is God,

in the heart of the sea. God is our ref - uge and strength.
God's cit - y stands se - cure. God is our ref - uge and strength.
Lord of heav - en and earth. God is our ref - uge and strength.

May be sung with bass pedal tone on E throughout.

*Original title

Text: Arlyn Friesen Epp, based on Psalm 46
Music: Arlyn Friesen Epp

27 God of the Bible

FRESH AS THE MORNING* 55. 54. 55. 54 with refrain

1 God of the Bi - ble, God in the Gos-pel, hope seen in Je-sus,
2 God in our strug-gles, God in our hun-ger, suf - fer-ing with us,
3 Those with-out sta - tus, those who are noth-ing, you have made roy-al,
4 Not by your fin - ger, not by your an-ger will our world or - der
5 Hope we must car - ry, shin-ing and cer-tain through all our tur-moil,

hope yet to come, you are our cen - ter, day-light or dark-ness,
tak - ing our part, still you em-pow'r us, moth - er - ing Spir - it,
gift - ed with rights, cho - sen as part - ners, mid-wives of jus - tice,
change in a day, but by your peo - ple, fear - less and faith - ful,
ter - ror and loss, bond-ing us glad - ly one to the oth - er,

free - dom or pris - on, you are our home.
feed - ing, sus - tain - ing, from your own heart.
birth - ing new sys - tems, light - ing new lights.
small pa - per lan - terns, light - ing the way.
till our world chang - es fac - ing the cross.

*Original title

Text: Shirley Erena Murray
Copyright © 1996 Hope Publishing Company, Carol Stream, IL 60188. All rights reserved. Used by permission.
Music: Tony E. Alonso
Copyright © 2001 GIA Publications, Inc.

28 We worship God the Rock

GENEVA 124 (OLD 124th) 10 10. 10 10 10

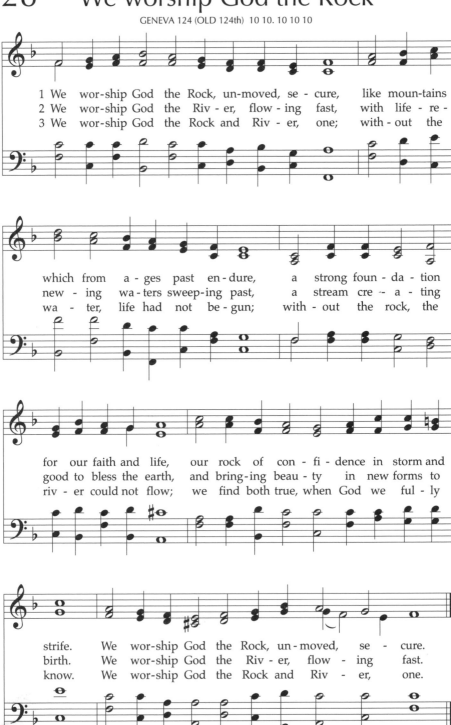

1 We wor-ship God the Rock, un-moved, se - cure, like moun-tains
2 We wor-ship God the Riv - er, flow-ing fast, with life - re -
3 We wor-ship God the Rock and Riv - er, one; with - out the

which from a - ges past en-dure, a strong foun - da - tion
new - ing wa - ters sweep-ing past, a stream cre - a - ting
wa - ter, life had not be - gun; with - out the rock, the

for our faith and life, our rock of con - fi - dence in storm and
good to bless the earth, and bring-ing beau - ty in new forms to
riv - er could not flow; we find both true, when God we ful - ly

strife. We wor-ship God the Rock, un-moved, se - cure.
birth. We wor-ship God the Riv - er, flow - ing fast.
know. We wor-ship God the Rock and Riv - er, one.

Text: Albert F. Bayly
Music: Louis Bourgeois, *Genevan Psalter*, 1551; harmonized by Claude Goudimel, *Les Pseaumes...*, 1565

You are all we have

56. 86

Text: Francis Patrick O'Brien
Music: Francis Patrick O'Brien
Copyright © 1992 G.I.A. Publications, Inc.

30 Jesus Christ is waiting

NOEL NOUVELET 11 11. 10 11

1 Je - sus Christ is wait - ing, wait - ing in the streets;
2 Je - sus Christ is rag - ing, rag - ing in the streets,
3 Je - sus Christ is heal - ing, heal - ing in the streets;
4 Je - sus Christ is danc - ing, danc - ing in the streets,
5 Je - sus Christ is call - ing, call - ing in the streets,

1 no one is his neigh-bor, all a - lone he eats.
2 where in - jus - tice spi - rals and real hope re - treats.
3 cur - ing those who suf - fer, touch-ing those he greets.
4 where each sign of ha - tred he, with love, de - feats.
5 "Who will join my jour-ney? I will guide their feet."

1 Lis - ten, Lord Je - sus, I am lone - ly too.
2 Lis - ten, Lord Je - sus, I am an - gry too.
3 Lis - ten, Lord Je - sus, I have pit - y too.
4 Lis - ten, Lord Je - sus, I should tri - umph too.
5 Lis - ten, Lord Je - sus, let my fears be few.

1 Make me, friend or strang-er, fit to wait on you.
2 In the king-dom's caus-es let me rage with you.
3 Let my care be ac-tive, heal-ing just like you.
4 Where good con-quers e - vil let me dance with you.
5 Walk one step be - fore me; I will fol - low you.

He came down

31

HE CAME DOWN LM

1 He came down that we may have love; he
2 He came down that we may have peace; he
3 He came down that we may have joy; he

came down that we may have love; he came down that we may
came down that we may have peace; he came down that we may
came down that we may have joy; he came down that we may

Leader (omit last time)
Why did he come?

have love; hal-le-lu-jah for ev-er-more.
have peace; hal-le-lu-jah for ev-er-more.
have joy; hal-le-lu-jah for ev-er-more.

Text: Cameroon traditional
Music: Cameroon traditional; arranged by John L. Bell
Arrangement copyright © 1990 WGRG The Iona Community (Scotland).
Used by permission of GIA Publications, Inc., exclusive agent.

32 If you believe and I believe

ZIMBABWE Irregular

If you be-lieve and I be-lieve and we to-geth-er pray, the

Ho-ly Spir-it must come down and set God's peo-ple free, and

set God's peo-ple free, and set God's peo-ple free; the

Ho-ly Spir-it must come down and set God's peo-ple free.

Text: Zimbabwe traditional
Music: Zimbabwe traditional; adapt. of English traditional, as taught by Tarasai; arranged by John L. Bell
Arrangement copyright © 1991 WGRG The Iona Community (Scotland).
Used by permission of GIA Publications, Inc., exclusive agent.

Come, Holy Spirit, descend

LEADER:

1 Come, Holy Spirit.

2 Come, Breath of Heaven.

3 Come, Word of Mercy.

4 Come, Fire of Judgment.

5 Come, Great Creator.

6 Come to unite us.

7 Come to disturb us.

8 Come to inspire us.

(other invocations ad lib)

Text: John L. Bell
Music: John L. Bell

34 Loving Spirit

OMNI DIE 87. 87

1,5 Lov - ing Spir - it, lov - ing Spir - it, you have
2 Like a moth - er you en - fold me, hold my
3 Like a fa - ther you pro - tect me. Teach me
4 Friend and lov - er, in your close - ness I am

cho - sen me to be; you have drawn me to your
life with - in your own. Feed me with your ver - y
the dis - cern - ing eye. Hoist me up up - on your
known and held and blest: in your prom - ise is my

won - der, you have set your sign on me.
bod - y, form me of your flesh and bone.
shoul - der, let me see the world from high.
com - fort, in your pres - ence I may rest.

Text: Shirley Erena Murray
Copyright © 1987 The Hymn Society; admin. Hope Publishing Company, Carol Stream, IL 60188.
All rights reserved. Used by permission.
Music: melody from *Gross Catolisch Gesangbuch*, 1631; harmonized by William Smith Rockstro

O Breath of Life

SPIRIT WIND 98. 98

1 O Breath__ of Life, come sweep - ing through us, re -
2 O Wind__ of God, come bend us, break us, till
3 O Spir - it of Love, come breathe with - in us, re -

vive your church with life and pow'r;
hum - bly we con - fess our need;
new - ing thought and will and heart;

O Breath of Life, come, cleanse, re - new us, and
then in your ten - der - ness re - make us, re -
come, Love of Christ, a - fresh to win us, re -

fit your church to meet this hour.
vive, re - store – for this we plead.
vive your church in ev - ery part!

For a four-part texture, tenors can double the melody an octave lower, and altos can double the bass line an octave higher.

Text: Elizabeth Ann P. Head, alt.
Music: James E. Clemens, 2001

36 Long before my journey's start

WISDOM, MY ROAD* Irregular

1 Long be-fore my jour-ney's start, when in my youth I
2 From the blos-som to the seed, long has she filled my
3 When I stretched my hands to the sky, when in des-pair my

searched in my heart, I would pray for her, wait for her,
cup in need, may I cling to her vine, taste of her wine,
soul raised a cry, I was saved by her gaze, led in her ways,

Wis-dom, my road, my goal, and my star.
Wis-dom, my life, my per-fect de-sign.
Wis-dom, my love, the light of my days.

*Original title

Text: Steven C. Warner, based on Ecclesiasticus 51:13-22
Music: Leslie Palmer Barnhart

Miren qué bueno
(Behold, how pleasant)

MIREN QUÉ BUENO 15. 14 with refrain

Refrain

Mir - en qué bue - no   qué   bue - no   es.
Be - hold, how pleas - ant,   how   good it   is!

Mir - en qué bue-no es cuan-do to - do el pue - blo es - tá   jun - to.
How good it is to   see God's peo - ple gath - ered all to - geth - er:

1 Es   co-mo a-cei - te   bue-no de - rra - ma - do   so-bre Aa - rón.
2 se   pa - ra-ce al ro - cío   o so - bre los mon - tes de   Síon.
3 por - que el Se - ñor ahi man-da vi-da e - ter - na y ben - di - ción.

1 fine   as the pre-cious oil___ run-ning down on   Aa-ron's   beard.
2 like   the re-fresh-ing dew up-on the moun-tain of the   Lord.
3 there the Lord sends a bless-ing and e - ter - nal life for   all.

Text: Pablo Sosa, based on Psalm 133, alt.
Music: Pablo Sosa
    Text and Music copyright © Pablo Sosa

38 Beloved, God's chosen

ST. CATHERINE'S COURT 12 11. 12 11

1 Be - lov - ed, God's cho - sen, put on as a gar - ment com -
2 With - in, call forth Wis - dom, to dwell in you rich - ly; let
3 Be - lov - ed, God's cho - sen, put on as a gar - ment com -

pas - sion, for - give - ness, and good - ness of heart. A -
peace rule your hearts and that peace be of Christ. And
pas - sion, for - give - ness, and good - ness of heart. A -

bove all, be - fore all, let love be your rai - ment that
from the heart's cham - ber, be - lov - ed and ho - ly, let
bove all, be - fore all, let love be your rai - ment that

binds in - to one ev - 'ry dis - so - nant part.
sing - ing thanks - giv - ing to God ev - er rise.
binds in - to one ev - 'ry dis - so - nant part.

Ubi caritas (Where true love) 39

UBI CARITAS 12 12. 12 12 with refrain

Refrain

Fine

U - bi ca - ri - tas et a - mor De - us i - bi est.
Where true love and char-i-ty are found, God is al-ways there.

1 Since the love of Christ has brought us
2 There-fore when we gath - er as one
3 Bring us with your saints to be - hold

all to - geth - er, let us all re -
in Christ Je - sus, let our love en -
your great beau - ty, there to see you,

joice and be glad, now and al - ways.
fold each race, creed, ev - 'ry per - son.
Christ our God, throned in great glo - ry;

Let ev - 'ry - one love the Lord___ God,
Let en - vy, di - vi - sion and___ strife
there to pos - sess heav - en's peace and joy,

the liv - ing God; and with sin - cere hearts
cease a - mong us; may Christ our Lord dwell
your truth and love, for end - less a - ges

D.C.

let us love each oth - er now.
a - mong us in ev - 'ry heart.
of a - ges, world with - out end.

Text: Latin, 9th c.; translation by Richard Proulx
Translation copyright © 1975, 1986 GIA Publications, Inc.
Music: Chant, Mode VI

40   As rain from the clouds

AFTON WATER 11 11. 11 11D

1 As rain from the clouds will your word come to earth, as
2 As grain that is scat-tered your word has been sown on
3 As rays of the sun shall your word light the world, a-

snow from the heav-ens re - fresh - ing the land. Then
rocks and on road-ways, in good earth and sand. Make
wak - ing and warm - ing and heal - ing our land. Then

soft - en our soil that the good seed may grow and
fer - tile our soil that the good seed may grow and
shine in our hearts that the good seed may grow and

rip - en rich fruit to re - turn to your hand. We
rip - en rich fruit to re - turn to your hand. We
rip - en rich fruit to re - turn to your hand. We

praise you, our God, for the dew of your word; we
praise you, our God, for the seed of your word; we
praise you, our God, for the light of your word; we

thank you, good gar - d'ner, for your ten - der toil. We

bless you, best farm - er, for hun - dred - fold yield, for

har - vest of grace in our once - bar - ren soil.

Text: Delores Dufner OSB
    Copyright © 1983, 1998 admin. G.I.A. Publications, Inc.
Music: English traditional

Alleluia

88. 88

Al - le - lu - ia. Al - le - lu - ia. Al - le - lu -

ia. Al - le - lu - ia. Al - le - lu - ia. Al -

le - lu - ia. Al - le - lu - ia. Al - le - lu - ia.

Music: transcribed from the singing of George Mxadana by John L. Bell
Arrangement copyright © GIA Publications, Inc.

42 Listen, God is calling

NENO LAKE MUNGU

Lis - ten: lis - ten, God is call-ing, through the word in - vit-ing,

of - fer - ing for - give-ness, com - fort, and joy.

1 Je - sus tells his peo - ple: share the good news
2 Let none be for - got - ten through - out the world.
3 Help us to be faith-ful, stand - ing stead - fast,

that he came to save us___ and sets us free.
In the tri - une name of God go and bap - tize.
walk-ing in your pre - cepts,___ led by your Word.

Text: Tanzanian traditional; translation by Howard S. Olson, alt.
Translation copyright © Makumira University College, Tanzania
Music: Tanzanian traditional; arranged by Austin C. Lovelace
Arrangement copyright © Austin C. Lovelace

My faith has found a resting place 43

LANDAS 86. 86 with refrain

1 My faith has found a rest-ing place—not in de-vice or creed:
2 E - nough for me that Je-sus saves—this ends my fear and doubt:
3 My heart is lean-ing on the word—the writ-ten word of God:
4 My great Phy - si - cian heals the sick—the lost he came to save;

I trust the Ev - er - liv-ing One—his wounds for me shall plead.
a sin - ful soul I come to him—he'll nev - er cast me out.
sal - va - tion by my Sav-ior's name— sal - va-tion through his blood.
for me his pre - cious blood he shed— for me his life he gave.

Refrain

I need no oth - er ar - gu-ment, I need no oth - er plea;

it is e-nough that Je - sus died, and that he died for me.

Text: Lidie H. Edmunds
Music: André Grétry; arranged by William J. Kirkpatrick

44 The love of God

LOVE OF GOD 88. 88. 86. 86 with refrain

1 The love of God is great-er far than tongue or
2 When an-cient time shall pass a - way, and hu - man
3 Could we with ink the o - cean fill and were the

pen can ev - er tell; it goes be - yond the high - est
thrones and king-doms fall; when all on earth re - fuse to
skies of parch-ment made; were ev - 'ry stalk on earth a

star, and reach-es to the low - est hell. The guilt - y
pray, on rocks and hills and moun-tains call; God's love, so
quill, and ev - 'ry - one a scribe by trade; to write the

pair, bowed down with care, God gave his Son to win; his err-ing
sure shall still en - dure, all mea-sure-less and strong; re-deem-ing
love of God a - bove would drain the o - cean dry; nor could the

Text: F. M. Lehman, c. 1917, alt.
Music: F. M. Lehman c. 1917; arranged by Claudia Lehman Mays

child he rec - on - ciled,   and   par - doned from   his   sin.
grace   to Ad-am's race   the   saints' and   an - gels'   song.
scroll con - tain the   whole, though stretched from sky   to   sky.

Refrain

O love   of God,   how rich   and pure!   How mea - sure-

less   and   strong!   It shall   for - ev -   er-more   en-

dure   the saints' and   an -   gels'   song.

45 In the morning when I rise

GIVE ME JESUS 666. 4 with refrain

1 In the morn-ing when I rise, in the morn-ing when I
2 Dark___ mid-night was my cry, dark___ mid-night was my
3 Just a-bout the break of day, just a-bout the break of
4 Oh,___ when I come to die, oh,___ when I come to

rise, in the morn-ing when I rise, give me Je - sus.
cry, dark___ mid-night was my cry, give me Je - sus.
day, just a-bout the break of day, give me Je - sus.
die, oh,___ when I come to die, give me Je - sus.

Refrain

Give me Je - sus, give me Je - sus. You may

have all this world, give me Je - sus.

Text: Spiritual
Music: Spiritual; arranged by Wendell Whalum
Arrangement copyright © 1978 Lawson-Gould Music Publishers, Inc.

O breathe on me, O breath of God 46

ST. COLUMBA CM

1 O breathe on me, O breath of God, fill
2 O breathe on me, O breath of God, un-
3 O breathe on me, O breath of God, my
4 O breathe on me, O breath of God, so

me with life a - new, that I may love the
til my heart is pure; un - til my will is
will to yours in - cline, un - til this self - ish
shall I nev - er die, but live with you the

things you love, and do what you would do.
one with yours, to do and to en - dure.
part of me glows with your fire di - vine.
per - fect life of your e - ter - ni - ty.

Text: Edwin Hatch, *Between Doubt and Prayer*, 1878, alt.
Music: Irish melody, *Irish Church Hymnal*, 1873 or 1874

47 Oh, Lord have mercy

HAVE MERCY ON ME 55. 55

1 Oh,　Lord　have　mer　-　cy.
2 While　I　am　pray　-　ing,
3 While　I　am　wait　-　ing,
4 When　I'm　in　trou　-　ble,
5 I　am　your　child,_____

1 Oh,　Lord　have　mer　-　cy.
2 while　I　am　pray　-　ing,
3 while　I　am　wait　-　ing,
4 when　I'm　in　trou　-　ble,
5 I　am　your　child,_____

1 Oh,　Lord　have　mer　-　cy,　have
2 while　I　am　pray　-　ing,　have
3 while　I　am　wait　-　ing,　have
4 when　I'm　in　trou　-　ble,　have
5 I　am　your　child,_____　have

mer　-　cy　on　me.

Text: traditional
Music: traditional; arranged by Joseph Joubert
　　　Arrangement copyright © 2000 G.I.A. Publications, Inc.

Our Father, which art in heaven 48

WEST INDIAN Irregular

Leader

F   C   F   C

1 Our_____ Fa - ther,   which art   in   heav - en,
2 Done   on___   earth   as   it   is   in   heav - en,
3 And   for -   give_____   all   our   tres - pass - es,
4 Lead_____   us   not   in - to_____   temp - ta - tion,
5 Thine   is   the   king - dom,   pow - er   and   glo - ry,
6 A -   men,   a -   men,_____   a - men,_____

All (in harmony)

F   C   F

hal - lowed   be   thy   name.

Leader

F/C   Gm/F   F/C   Gm/F   C

1 Thy___   king - dom   come,___   thy   will   be___   done,___
2 give___   us   this   day_____   our   dai - ly___   bread,
3 as___   we   for - give those   who   tres - pass a - gainst   us,
4 _____   but   de - liv -   er   us   from___   e - vil,
5 for___   ev - er   and_____   for   ev - er -   more,___
6 a -   men,   a - men,_____   a - men,   a -   men,_____

All (in harmony)

F   B♭   C   F

hal - lowed   be   thy   name.

Text: based on Matthew 6:9-13
Music: West Indian melody

49 Rain down

All of God's works are so wor - thy of trust.
live in the kind - ness and joy of God's wing.
you are the wa - ter of life that we thirst.

ooh,

God's mer - cy falls on the just and the right;
God will pro - tect us from dark - ness and death;
Grant that your love and your peace touch our hearts,

ah,

full of God's love is the earth.
God will not leave us to starve.
all of our hope lies in you.

mf

1 Full of God's love is the earth.
2 God will not leave us to starve.
3 All of our hope lies in you.

mf

50 Keep me safe, O God

Verses

1 I say to God, "you are my on - ly God,
2 I find in God al - ways my cup of joy;

3 I bless my God: God who has coun - seled me.
4 I keep my God al - ways be - fore my eyes;
5 And so my heart al - ways is glad in God;

6 For you will not ev - er a - ban - don me,
7 The path of life you have re - vealed to me,

1 I have no good ex - cept in you."
2 and God will keep my life se - cure.

3 At night my heart gives coun - sel too.
4 with God be - side me I'm se - cure.
5 my bod - y too shall dwell se - cure.

6 or let your ser - vant lose the path.
7 and in your pres - ence is my joy.

Text: John Foley, SJ; based on Psalm 16
Music: John Foley, SJ

As tranquil streams

WINCHESTER NEW   LM

1 As   tran - quil streams that   meet   and   merge   and
2 Free   from   the   bonds   that   bind   the   mind   to
3 A   free - dom   that   re - veres   the   past,   but
4 Pro - phet - ic church, the   fu - ture waits your

flow   as   one   to   seek the   sea,   our   kin - dred hearts and
nar - row thought and life - less creed; free from a   so - cial
trusts the   dawn - ing   fu - ture more; and bids the soul, in
lib - er - at - ing min - is - try; go   for - ward in   the

minds u - nite   to   build a   church that shall be free —
code   that fails to   serve the   cause of   hu - man need:
search of   truth, ad - ven - ture bold - ly and   ex - plore.
power of   love, pro - claim the   truth that makes us   free.

Text: Marion Franklin Ham, 1933
Music: *Musicalisch Handbuch...*, 1690, arranged by William H. Havergal, *Old Church Psalmody*, 1847

52 Jesus, help us live in peace

UNITY* 77. 77

Refrain: Je - sus, help us live in peace,
1 Man - y times we don't a - gree
2 How we long for pow'r and fame,

from our blind-ness set us free.
on what's right or wrong to do.
seek - ing ev - 'ry earth - ly thing.

Fill us with your heal - ing love.
It's so hard to real - ly see
We for - get the one who came

Help us live in u - ni - ty.
from the oth - er's point of view.
as a ser - vant, not a king.

*Original title

Text: Gerald Derstine, based on Philippians 2:1-8
Music: Gerald Derstine

O God in heaven

HALAD 55. 55. 55. 54

1 O God in heav - en,   grant to your chil - dren   mer - cy and
2 Je - sus, re - deem - er,   help us re - mem - ber   your pain and
3 Spir - it un - end - ing,   give us your bless - ing: strength for the

bless - ing,   songs nev - er ceas - ing,   grace to in - vite us,   peace to u-
pas - sion,   your res - ur - rec - tion,   your call to   fol - low,   your love to-
wea - ry,   help for the need - y,   hope for the scorn - ful,   peace for the

nite   us—   O God in heav - en,   au - thor of love.
mor - row—   Je - sus, re - deem - er,   sav - ior, and friend.
mourn - ful—   Spir - it un - end - ing,   com - fort and guide.

Text: Elena G. Maquiso; translated by D. T. Niles, alt.
Music: Philippines traditional; adapted by Elena G. Maquiso; arr. *Cantate Domino,* 1980
         Text and Music copyright © 1962 Elena G. Maquiso
         Translation copyright © 1964 Christian Conference of Asia. All rights reserved.
         Arrangement copyright © 1980 World Council of Churches

54

Longing for light

CHRIST, BE OUR LIGHT   98. 96 with refrain

1 Long-ing for light,— we wait in dark-ness.
2 Long-ing for peace,— our world is trou-bled.
3 Long-ing for food,— man-y are hun-gry.
4 Long-ing for shel-ter, man-y are home-less.
5 Man-y the gifts,— man-y the peo-ple,

1 Long-ing for truth,— we turn to you.
2 Long-ing for hope,— man-y de-spair.
3 Long-ing for wa-ter, man-y still thirst.
4 Long ing for warmth,— man-y are cold.
5 man-y the hearts that yearn to be-long.

1 Make us your own,— your ho-ly peo-ple,
2 Your word a-lone— has pow'r to save us.
3 Make us your bread,— bro-ken for oth-ers,
4 Make us your build-ing, shel-ter-ing oth-ers,
5 Let us be ser-vants to one an-oth-er,

1 light for the world to see.
2 Make us your liv-ing voice.
3 shared un-til all are fed.
4 walls made of liv-ing stone.
5 mak-ing your king-dom come.

Refrain

Christ, be our light!— Shine in our

Text: Bernadette Farrell
Music: Bernadette Farrell

hearts. Shine through the dark - ness.
Shine in our hearts. Shine through the dark - ness.

Christ, be our light! Shine in your church

gath - ered to - day.

Healing balm, forgiving Lord 55

Heal-ing balm, for-giv-ing Lord, Ky - ri - e e - le - i - son.

56 Make me a channel of your peace

loved as to love, with all my soul.

Optional descant, verse 4

Ah, ah,

ah, ah.

SPANISH

1 Hazme un instrumento de tu paz, donde haya odio, lleve yo tu amor,
   donde haya injuria, tu perdón, Señor, donde haya duda, fe en ti.

2 Hazme un instrumento de tu paz, que lleve tu esperanza por doquier,
   donde haya oscuridad lleve tu luz, donde haya pena, tu gozo, Señor.

3 Maestro ayúdame a nunca buscar ser consolado si no consolar,
   ser ententido sino entender, ser amado sino amar.

4 Hazme un instrumento de tu paz, es perdonando que nos das perdón,
   es dando a todos que tú nos das, y muriendo es que volvemos a nacer.

57 Mayenziwe (Your will be done)

Text: from the Lord's Prayer
Music: South African traditional, as taught by George Mxadana; transcribed John L. Bell, 1988

Who has known the mind of Jesus? 58

JEG RÅDE VIL ALLE   87.87 with refrain

1 Who has known the mind of Je-sus? Who has been his
2 Ho - ly Je-sus, help us all to lis-ten for our

coun - sel - or? Who has known what real - ly pleas - es
neigh - bors' cry. Give us ears to hear their call and

him whom an - gel hosts a - dore?
an - swer quick - ly, "Here am I!" Je - sus, help us

see! Give us eyes that see, through the dark and

cloud-y night, a glimpse of your e - ter - ni - ty.

59

Confitemini Domino
(Come and fill our hearts)

Irregular

Latin: Con - fi - te - mi - ni Do - mi - no
English: Come and fill our hearts with your peace.
French: Viens rem - plir nos coeurs de ta paix.
Spanish: Ven y lle - na - nos de tu paz.

quo - ni - am___ bo - nus. Con - fi - te - mi - ni
You a - lone, O Lord, are ho - ly. Come and fill our hearts
Toi seul, tu es saint oh Seig - neur. Viens rem - plir nos coeurs
So - lo tu, oh Dios, sos San - to. Ven y lle - na - nos

Do - mi - no, al - le - lu - - - ia.
with your peace, al - le - lu - - - ia.
de ta paix, al - le - lu - - - ia.
de tu paz, a - le - lu - - - ia.

Text: Jacques Berthier; translated by Jessica Goldschmidt (French) and Betty Puricelli (Spanish)
Music: Jacques Berthier

Lord of all good

GENEVA 124 (OLD 124th) 10 10. 10 10 10

Lord of all good, our gifts we bring to you;

use them your ho - ly pur - pose to ful - fill;

to - kens of love and pledg - es brought a - new,

that our whole life is of - fered to your will.

Lord of all good, our gifts we bring to you.

61 How can we be silent

HOW CAN WE BE SILENT Irregular

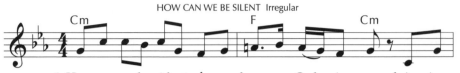

1 How can we be si-lent when we know our God is near, bring-ing
2 How can we be si-lent when our God has con-quered death, stretch-ing
3 How can we be si-lent as we turn our eyes a - way and ig -
4 How can we be si-lent, not give praise with all our hearts, for Christ
5 How can we be si-lent when our souls are filled with awe at the

1 light to those in dark-ness, to the worth-less, end-less worth?
2 out his arms to suf - fer so that we might have new life?
3 nore the poor and bro-ken who lie bleed-ing in the street?
4 Je - sus is our Sav - ior and com - pas - sion is our king?
5 beau-ty of cre - a - tion and the mer - cy of our Lord?

1 How can we be si-lent when we are the voice of Christ, speak-ing
2 How can we be si-lent when we know that Je - sus rose, and will
3 How can we be si-lent when we're called to heal and serve in the
4 How can we be si-lent when God gave us life to be vi - brant
5 How can we be si-lent when we yearn to sing new songs? In our

1 jus - tice to the na-tions, breath-ing love to all the earth?
2 come a - gain in glo - ry, end-ing suf - fer - ing and strife?
3 im - age of Lord Je - sus, who has stooped to wash our feet?
4 in - stru-ments of wor-ship, made to laugh and dance and sing?
5 hearts a fire is burn-ing and it will not be ig-nored!

Refrain*

None can stop the Spir-it burn-ing now in - side us. We will shape the

fu - ture. We will not be si - lent!

*May be sung as a canon.

Text: Michael Mahler
Music: Michael Mahler
Copyright © 2003 GIA Publications, Inc.

Christ's is the world

DREAM ANGUS 89. 99 with refrain

G   C   Dsus D

1 Christ's is the world___ in which we move,
2 Feel for the peo - ple we most a - void,
3 Feel for the par - ents who've lost their child,
4 Feel for the lives___ by life con - fused,

Bm   C   G

Christ's are the folk___ we're sum-moned to love,
strange or be - reaved___ or nev - er em - ployed;
feel for the wom - en whom men have de - filed,
rid - dled with doubt,___ in lov - ing a - bused;

Bm   Em7   Am   Bm

Christ's is the voice___ which calls us to care, and
feel for the wom - en, and feel for the men who
feel for the ba - by for whom there's no breast, and
feel for the lone - ly heart, con - scious of sin, which

G   Em   C   Dsus D

Christ is the one___ who meets___ us here.
fear that their liv - ing is all___ in vain.
feel for the wea - ry who find___ no rest.
longs to be pure___ but fears to be - gin.

G   Am   C   Dsus D

To the lost Christ shows his face;

Bm   C   G

to the un - loved he gives his em - brace;

Bm   Em7   Am   Bm

to those who cry in pain or dis - grace, Christ

G   Em   C   Dsus D

makes, with his friends, a touch - ing place.

Text: John L. Bell
    Copyright © 1989 WGRG The Iona Community (Scotland). Used by permission of GIA Publications, Inc., exclusive agent.
Music: Scottish folk song

63 Lord, you give the great commission

HYFRYDOL 87. 87D

1 Lord, you give the great com-mis-sion: "Heal the sick and
2 Lord, you call us to your ser-vice: "In my name bap-
3 Lord, you make the com-mon ho-ly: "This my bod-y,
4 Lord, you show us love's true mea-sure: "Fa-ther, what they
5 Lord, you bless with words as-sur-ing: "I am with you

1 preach the word." Lest the church ne-glect its mis-sion
2 tize and teach." That the world may trust your prom-ise,
3 this my blood." Let us all, for earth's true glo-ry,
4 do, for-give." Yet we hoard as pri-vate trea-sure
5 to the end." Faith and hope and love re-stor-ing,

1 and the gos-pel go un-heard, help us wit-ness
2 life a bun-dant meant for each, give us all new
3 dai-ly lift life heav-en-ward, ask-ing that the
4 all that you so free-ly give. May your care and
5 may we serve as you in-tend, and, a-mid the

1 to your pur - pose with re - newed in - teg - ri - ty:
2 fer - vor, draw us clos - er in com - mu - ni - ty:
3 world a - round us share your chil - dren's lib - er - ty:
4 mer - cy lead us to a just so - ci - e - ty:
5 cares that claim us, hold in mind e - ter - ni - ty:

With the Spir - it's gifts em - pow'r us

for the work of min - is - try.

64 Somos el cuerpo de Cristo (We are the body of Christ)

Text: Jaime Cortez and Bob Hurd
Music: Jaime Cortez

Verses

Solo

1 Dios vie-ne al mun-do a tra - vés de no-so-tros.
  mun - do a cum - plir la mi - sión de la I - gle - sia,
2 Ca - da per - so - na es par - te del rei - no;
  To - das las ra - zas que ha - bi - tan la tie - rra,
3 nues - tras ac - cio - nes re - fle - jen jus - ti - cia;
  Va - mos al mun - do a cui - dar su re - ba - ño.

All

So - mos el cuer - po de Cris - to.

Solo

God is re - vealed when we love one an - oth - er.
Bring - ing the light of God's mer - cy to oth - ers,
Put - ting a stop to all dis - crim - i - na - tion,
All are in - vit - ed to feast in the ban - quet.
Stop - ping a - buse and re - liev - ing the hun - gry,
Serv - ing each oth - er we build up the king - dom;

All

1 F *Solo*   2 F   D.C.

We are the bod - y of Christ.   (1) Al   Christ.
                                 (2)
                                 (3)

65 Let justice flow like streams

ST. THOMAS (WILLIAMS) SM

1 Let jus-tice flow like streams of spark-ling wa-ter pure, en-
2 Let righ-teous-ness roll on as oth-ers' cares we heed, an
3 So may God's plumb line, straight, de - fine our mea-sure true, and

a - bling growth, re - fresh-ing life, a - bun-dant, cleans-ing, sure.
ev - er - flow - ing stream of faith trans - lat - ed in - to deed.
jus - tice, right, and peace per-vade this world our whole life through.

Text: Jane Parker Huber, *A Singing Faith*; based on Amos 5:14-15, 24; 7:7-8
Copyright © 1984 Jane Parker Huber. Used by permission of Westminster / John Knox Press.
Music: Aaron Williams, *The Universal Psalmodist*, 1763

If the war goes on

THE ROAD TO BASRAH 58. 57. 58. 5

Solo	1	If	the	war	goes	on	and the	chil - dren die	of	hun - ger,
Men	2	If	the	war	goes	on	and the	truth is	tak - en	hos - tage,
Women	3	If	the	war	goes	on	and the	dai - ly bread	is	ter - ror,
Solo	4	If	the	war	goes	on	and the	rich in - crease their for - tunes,
All	5	If	the	war	goes	on,	will we	close the doors	to	heav - en?

1	and the	old	men	weep,	for the	young men	are	no	more,
2	and new	ter - rors	lead	to the	need	to	eu - phe - mize;
3	and the	voice - less	poor	take the	road	as	ref - u - gees;
4	and the	arms	sales	soar	as new	weap - ons	are	dis - played;
5	If	the	war	goes	on,	will we	breach the	gates	of	hell?

1	and the	wom - en	learn how	to	dance with - out	a	part - ner,
2	when the	calls	for	peace	are de - clared un - pa - tri - ot - ic,
3	when a	na - tion's	pride	des - tines	mil - lions	to	be home - less,
4	when a	fer - tile	field	turns to	no - man's - land	to - mor - row,
5	If	the	war	goes	on,	will we	ev - er	be	for - giv - en?

1	who	will	keep	the	score?
2	who'll	ex -	pose	the	lies?
3	who	will	heed	their	pleas?
4	who'll	ap -	prove	such	trade?
5	If	the	war	goes	on...

Text: John L. Bell and Graham Maule, 1997, revised 2002
Music: John L. Bell, 1997

67 Let there be light, Lord God

OLD HUNDREDTH LM

1 Let there be light, Lord God of hosts!
2 With - in our pas - sioned hearts in - still
3 Give us the peace of vi - sion clear
4 Let woe and waste of war - fare cease,

Let there be wis - dom on the earth!
the calm that ends all strain and strife.
to see each oth - er's good, our own,
that use - ful la - bor yet may build

Let broad hu - man - i - ty have birth!
Make us your min - is - ters of life.
to joy and suf - fer not a - lone:
its homes with love and laugh - ter filled!

Let there be deeds in - stead of boasts.
Purge us from lusts that curse and kill.
the love that casts a - side all fear.
God, give your way - ward chil - dren peace!

Text: William M. Vories, 1908, *Advocate of Peace*, 1909, alt.
Music: Louis Bourgeois, *Genevan Psalter*, 1551

O hear, my people

L'CHA DODI LM

1 O hear, my peo - ple, hear me well: "I
2 Then source of peace, lead us to peace, a
3 May deeds we do in - scribe our names as

have no need for sac - ri - fice; but
place pro - found, and whol - ly true. And
bless - ings in the Book of Life. O

mer - cy, lov - ing kind - ness shall a -
lead us to a mas - ter - y o'er
source of peace, lead us to heal. O

lone for life and good suf - fice."
drives in us that war pur - sue.
source of peace, lead us from strife.

Text: from Rabbi Nachman of Bratzlav
Music: L. Lewandowski

69

Cuando el pobre
(When the poor ones)

EL CAMINO 12 11. 12.11 11

1 Cuan-do el po - bre na - da
2 Cuan-do un hom - bre su - fre y
1 When the poor ones, who have
2 When com - pas - sion gives the

tie - ne y aún re - par - te, cuan-do un
lo - gra su con - sue - lo, cuan-do es-
noth-ing, still are giv - ing; when the
suf - f'ring con - so - la - tion; when ex -

hom - bre pa - sa sed y a-gua nos da, cuan-do el
pe - ra y no se can - sa de es-pe - rar, cuan-do a-
thirst - y pass the cup, wa - ter to share; when the
pect - ing brings to birth hope that was lost; when we

dé - bil a su her - ma - no for - ta - le - ce,
ma - mos, aun-que el o - dio nos ro - dé - e,
wound - ed of - fer oth - ers strength and heal - ing:
choose love, not the ha - tred all a - round us:

Refrain/Estribillo

va Dios mis - mo en nues-tro mis - mo ca - mi -
we see God, here by our side, walk - ing our

nar. Va Dios mis - mo en nues - tro
way; we see God, here by our

Text: J. A. Olivar (Spanish), Martin A. Seltz (English); based on Matthew 25 and Luke 24
Music: Miguel Manzano and J. A. Olivar

mis - mo   ca - mi - nar.
side, walk - ing our way.

SPANISH

3 Cuando crece la alegría y nos inunda,
   cuando dicen nuestros labios la verdad,
   cuando amamos el sentir de los sencillos,
   Estribillo

4 Cuando abunda el bien y llena los hogares,
   cuando un hombre donde hay guerra pone paz,
   cuando "hermano" le llamamos al extraño,
   Estribillo

ENGLISH

3 When our spirits, like a chalice, brim wtih gladness;
   when our voices, full and clear, sing out the truth;
   when our longings, free from envy, seek the humble:
   Refrain

4 When the goodness poured from heaven
      fills our dwellings;
   when the nations work to change war into peace;
   when the stranger is accepted as our neighbor:
   Refrain

Pah Jesu song ern kha
(Jesus, you have called us)

70

65. 44

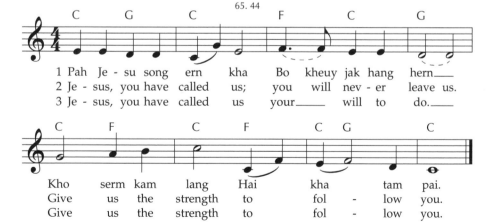

1 Pah Je - su song   ern   kha   Bo   kheuy jak hang hern___
2 Je - sus, you have called us;   you will nev - er   leave us.
3 Je - sus, you have called us   your___ will to   do.___

Kho   serm kam   lang   Hai   kha   tam   pai.
Give   us   the   strength to   fol - low you.
Give   us   the   strength to   fol - low you.

Pronunciation: Pah Yay-soo song ehrn kah Boh koy zhahk hahng hehrn
                Kho serm kahm lahng High kah tam pie.

Text: Doug Krehbiel and Jude Krehbiel, based on I Corinthians 15:58; inspired by conversation with Kuaying Teng
        Laotian translation by Kuaying Teng
Music: Doug Krehbiel and Jude Krehbiel
        Text and Music copyright © 2003 Doug Krehbiel and Jude Krehbiel

71 Alleluia, the Great Storm is over

THE GREAT STORM IS OVER* 11 11. 11 11 with refrain

Refrain

Al - le - lu - ia, the Great Storm is o - ver, lift

up your wings and fly.

1 The thun - der and light-ning gave voice__ to the night, the
2 Sweet-ness in the air__ and jus-tice on the wind,
3 Re - lease__ for the cap-tives, and end__ to the wars, new
4 Hush__ lit - tle ba - by, let go__ of your fear, the

lit - tle lame__ child cried a - loud in her fright.
laugh-ter in the house where the mourn-ers had been; the
streams__ in the des - ert, new hope for the poor, the
Lord__ loves his own and your moth - er is here; the

Hush,__ lit - tle ba - by, a sto - ry I'll tell of a
deaf__ shall have mu - sic, the blind have new eyes, the__
lit - tle lame__ chil-dren will dance as they sing, and__
child__ fell a - sleep as the lan - tern did burn, the__

love that has van-quished the pow - ers of hell.
stan - dards of death tak - en down by sur - prise.
play with the bears and the li - ons in spring.
moth - er sang on till her bride-groom's re - turn.

*Original title

Text: Bob Franke
Music: Bob Franke

One is the body

PEACOCK 10 10 12

1 One is the bod - y and one is the Head,
2 Christ who a - scend - ed to heav - en a - bove
3 Gifts have been giv - en well suit - ed to each,
4 Called to his ser - vice are wom - en and men

one is the Spir - it by whom we are led;
is the same Je - sus whose na - ture is love,
some to be proph - ets, to pas - tor or preach,
so that his bod - y might ev - er a - gain

one God and Fa - ther, one faith and one call for
who once de - scend - ed to bring to this earth new
some, through the Gos - pel, to chal - lenge, con - vert and
wit - ness through wor - ship, through deed and through word to

all.
birth.
teach.
Christ our Lord.

Text: John L. Bell
Music: John L. Bell

73 The Lord lift you up

BENEDICTION* 55. 55. 54. 55

The Lord lift you up, the Lord take your
hand, the Lord lead you forth, and cause you to
stand, se - cure in God's word, seek - ing God's
face, a - bound-ing in love, a - bid - ing in

1 E
grace. The

Final E
grace.

*Original title

Text: Patricia J. Shelly
Music: Patricia J. Shelly; arranged by Dennis Friesen-Carper
Text and Music copyright © 1983 Patricia J. Shelly

74 Now go in peace

JUNKANOO Irregular

Canon

Now go in peace, now go in love,
from the Fa - ther a - bove. Je - sus Christ the Son

Text: Michael Mair
Copyright © Panel on Worship, Church of Scotland
Music: Caribbean folk tune

stay with you till the day is done. Ho - ly Spir - it en -
cir - cle you in all you think and do. Go in
peace. God's bless - ing be with us. A - men.

Be still

75

Leader 1 Be still, *All* Irregular
1 Be still, God will fight your bat - tles.

Leader Be still, *All*
Be still, God will fight your bat - tles.

Leader Be still, *All*
Be still, God will fight your bat - tles.

God will fight your bat - tles if you just keep still.

Percussion pattern:

Hand-claps

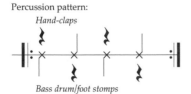

Bass drum/foot stomps

2 Keep a prayin', God will fight your battles ...
3 Keep a waitin', God will fight your battles ...
4 Keep a singin', God will fight your battles ...
5 I'm a witness, God will fight your battles ...

Text: African-American traditional
Music: African-American traditional; arranged by Nolan Williams Jr.
Arrangement copyright © 2000 GIA Publications, Inc.

76 The Lord bless you and keep you

FAREWELL ANTHEM Irregular

The Lord bless you and keep you, the Lord lift his coun-te-nance up-on you, and give you peace, and give you peace, and give you and give you peace, the Lord make his face to shine up-peace, the Lord make his and be gra - cious un-to you, be gra-cious, on you, and be gra-cious, and be gra-cious,

Text: Numbers 6:24-26
Music: Peter C. Lutkin, 1900

77 The peace of the earth be with you

LA PAZ DE LA TIERRE 87. 97. 76

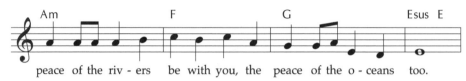

The peace of the earth be with you, the peace of the heav-ens too; the

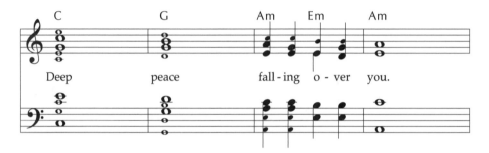

peace of the riv-ers be with you, the peace of the o-ceans too.

Deep peace fall-ing o-ver you.

God's peace grow-ing in you.

Text: Guatemalan traditional; translated by Christine Carson
Music: Guatemalan folk melody

Sizohamba naye
(We will walk with God)

96. 96. 66. 66

Si - zo-ham - ba na - ye, wo wo wo, si - zo-ham - ba na - ye.
We will walk___ with God, my broth-ers, we will walk___with God.
We will walk___ with God, my sis-ters, we will walk___with God.

Ngom-hla wen-ja - bu - la   si - zo-ham - ba na - ye.
We   will go re - joic-ing   till the king - dom has come.

Ngom-hla wen-ja - bu - la   si - zo-ham - ba na - ye.
We   will go re - joic-ing   till the king - dom has come.

Text: Swaziland traditional; translated by John L. Bell
Music: Swaziland traditional; transcribed by the Swedish Youth Exchange project, "Meeting Swaziland"
    Text and Music copyright © 2002 WGRG The Iona Community (Scotland).
    Used by permission of GIA Publications, Inc., exclusive agent.

79 As I went down to the river

Refrain   Irregular

1,3,5 As I went down to* the riv-er to pray,
2,4,6 As I went down to* the riv-er to pray,

stud-y-in' a-bout that good old way, and who shall wear the
stud-y-in' a-bout that good old way, and who shall wear the

Fine

star - ry crown. Good Lord, show me the way.
robe and crown. Good Lord, show me the way.

1 Oh, sis - ters, let's go down, let's go down,
2 Oh, broth-ers, let's go down, let's go down,
3 Oh, fa - thers, let's go down, let's go down,
5 Oh, sin - ners, let's go down, let's go down,

*Alternate phrase: down *in* the river

Text: American folk song
Music: American folk song; arranged by James E. Clemens, 2004
    Arrangement copyright © 2004 James E. Clemens

come on down.   Oh,____   sis - ters,   let's go
come on down.   Come on,   broth - ers,   let's go
come on down.   Oh,____   fa - thers,   let's go
come on down.   Oh,____   sin - ners,   let's go

D.C.

down,   down   to the riv - er to   pray.
down,   down   to the riv - er to   pray.
down,   down   to the riv - er to   pray.
down,   down   to the riv - er to   pray.

4 Oh,   moth-ers,   let's go down,   come on   down, don't you

wan-na go down.   Come on,   moth - ers,   let's   go

D.C.

down,   down   to the riv - er to   pray.

80 Christ be near at either hand

GARTEN 77. 77

1 Christ be near at ei - ther hand, Christ be - hind, be -
2 Christ be in my heart and mind, Christ with - in my
3 Christ my life and on - ly way, Christ my lan - tern

fore me stand; Christ with me where - e'er I go,
soul en - shrined; Christ con - trol my way - ward heart;
night and day; Christ be my un - chang - ing friend,

Christ a - round, a - bove, be - low.
Christ a - bide and ne'er de - part.
guide and shep - herd to the end.

Text: Irish traditional, the Lorica of St. Patrick
Music: Irish traditional; arranged by Gerard Gillen

Take, O take me as I am

77.74

Take, O take me as I am; sum-mon out what I shall

be; set your seal up-on my heart and live in me.

Text: John L. Bell
Music: John L. Bell

Text and Music copyright © 1995 WGRG The Iona Community (Scotland).
Used by permission of GIA Publications, Inc., exclusive agent.

82 Water has held us

BUNESSAN 55. 54D

1 Wa - ter has held us, moved by cre - a - tion.
2 Wa - ter has saved us, as the sea part - ed
3 Wa - ter has cleansed us, bathed with for - give - ness,
4 Wa - ter has touched us, fresh on our fore - heads,

Out of dark cha - os, broke forth the light. Up from the del - uge,
for Is - rael's chil - dren, walled on each side. This love has led us,
has, with clear bless - ing, washed sin a - way. Jor - dan's strong cur - rents
show - ing an in - ward, spir - i - tual grace. In - to God's fam - 'ly,

show - ing God's prom - ise, has come a rain - bow, glad - den - ing sight.
helped us in trou - ble, on far ho - ri - zon, God's cloud our guide.
God's Son an - nounc - ing, made a be - gin - ning, bap - tis - mal day.
we have been wel - comed. As sons and daugh - ters, we take our place.

Text: R. Deane Postlethwaite, 1978
Copyright © Marjean Postlethwaite
Music: Gaelic melody; *Songs and Hymns of the Gael*, 1888; harmonized by Martin Shaw, alt.
Harmonization copyright © Oxford University Press, London

Take me to the water

TO THE WATER Irregular

1 Take me to the wa - ter, take me to the
wa - ter, take me to the wa -
ter to be bap - tized.

2 None but the righteous (3x)
shall see God.

3 I love Jesus. (3x)
Yes, I do.

4 In the name of Jesus (3x)
we shall be saved.

5 I know I got religion. (3x)
Yes, I do.

6 Glory, hallelujah, (3x)
to be baptized.

Text: African-American spiritual
Music: African-American spiritual

84 Jesus, offered up as bread

TABLE ROUND 77. 85

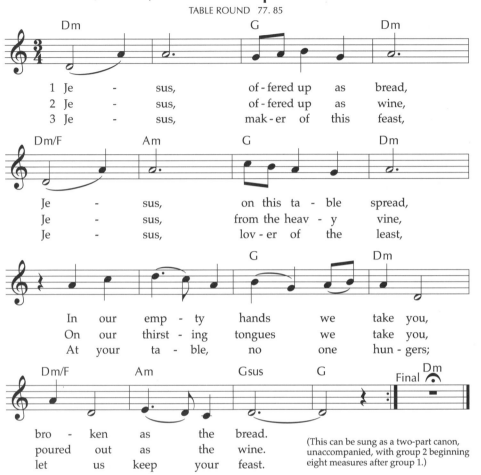

1 Je - sus, of-fered up as bread,
2 Je - sus, of-fered up as wine,
3 Je - sus, mak-er of this feast,

Je - sus, on this ta - ble spread,
Je - sus, from the heav - y vine,
Je - sus, lov-er of the least,

In our emp-ty hands we take you,
On our thirst-ing tongues we take you,
At your ta - ble, no one hun - gers;

bro - ken as the bread.
poured out as the wine.
let us keep your feast.

(This can be sung as a two-part canon,
unaccompanied, with group 2 beginning
eight measures after group 1.)

Version 2

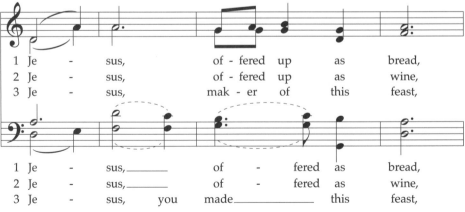

1 Je - sus, of - fered up as bread,
2 Je - sus, of - fered up as wine,
3 Je - sus, mak - er of this feast,

1 Je - sus,_____ of - fered as bread,
2 Je - sus,_____ of - fered as wine,
3 Je - sus, you made_____ this feast,

Je - sus, on this ta - ble spread,
Je - sus, from the heav - y vine,
Je - sus, lov - er of the least,

Je - sus, the ta - ble spread,
Je - sus, the heav - y vine,
Je - sus, you love the least;

In our emp - ty hands we take you,
On our thirst - ing tongues we take you,
At your ta - ble, no one hun - gers;

In our emp - ty hands we take you,
On our thirst - ing tongues we take you,
At your ta - ble, no one hun - gers;

1, 2

bro - ken as the bread.
poured out as the wine.
let us keep your

bro - ken as the bread.
poured out as the wine.
let us keep your

3

feast. A - men.

feast. A - men.

85

Pan de Vida

Refrain   Irregular

*Pan de Vi- da, cuer- po del Se- ñor, cup of bless- ing, blood of Christ the Lord.

At this ta- ble the last shall be first. **Po- der es ser- vir, por- que Dios es a- mor.

To verses / mor. / Po- / mor.

*Bread of life, body of the Lord.

**Power is for service, because God is love.

Text: Bob Hurd and Pia Moriarty, based on John 13:1-15; Galatians 3:28-29
Music: Bob Hurd; accompaniment by Dominic MacAller
Text and Music copyright © 1988, 1997 Bob Hurd and Pia Moriarty. Published by OCP Publications, 5536 NE Hassalo, Portland, OR 97213. All rights reserved. Used with permission.

Verses

G · A7/G · G · A7/G

1 We are the dwell-ing of God,
2 Us - te - des me lla - man "Se - ñor," me in-
*2 You call me Teach - er and Lord;
3 There is no Jew___ or Greek;

G · A7/G · D · D9/C♯ · Bm

frag - ile and wound-ed and weak. We are the
cli - no a la - var - les los pies: Ha - gan lo
I, who have washed___ your feet. So you must
there is no slave___ or free; there is no

Bm/A · Esus · E7 · Em · F♯m

bod - y of Christ, called to be_____ the com -
mis - mo hu - mil - des, sir - vién - do - se
do as I do, so the great - est must be -
wom - an or man; on - ly heirs_____ of the

G · A · A7sus · A7 · D.C.

pas - sion of God._____
u - nos a o - tros.
come___ the least._____
prom - ise of God._____

*English translation of Spanish verse 2.

86

Taste and see

Irregular with refrain

1 I will bless the Lord at all times. Praise shall always be on my lips;
  my soul shall glory in the Lord for God has been so good to me.

2 Glorify the Lord with me. Together let us all praise God's name.
  I called the Lord who answered me; from all my troubles I was set free.

3 Worship the Lord, all you people. You'll want for nothing if you ask.
  Taste and see that the Lord is good; in God we need put all our trust.

Text: James E. Moore, based on Psalm 34:1-10
Music: James E. Moore
      Text and Music copyright © 1983 GIA Publications, Inc.

Put peace into each other's hands 87

ST. COLUMBA CM

1 Put peace in-to each oth-er's hands and
2 Put peace in-to each oth-er's hands with
3 Put peace in-to each oth-er's hands like
4 As at com-mu-nion, shape your hands in-
5 Put Christ in-to each oth-er's hands, he

1 like a trea-sure hold it, pro-tect it like a
2 lov-ing ex-pec-ta-tion; be gen-tle in your
3 bread we break for shar-ing; look peo-ple warm-ly
4 to a wait-ing cra-dle; the gift of Christ re-
5 is love's deep-est mea-sure; in love make peace, give

1 can-dle-flame, with ten-der-ness en-fold it.
2 words and ways, in touch with God's cre-a-tion.
3 in the eye: our life is meant for car-ing.
4 ceive, re-vere, u-nit-ed round the ta-ble.
5 peace a chance, and share it like a trea-sure.

Text: Fred Kaan
Music: Irish melody, *Irish Church Hymnal*, 1873 or 1874

88 Haleluya! Pelo tsa rona (Hallelujah! We sing your praises!)

HALELUYA! PELO TSA RONA Irregular

Ha - le - lu - ya! Pe - lo tsa ro - na, di tha -
Hal - le - lu - jah! We sing your prais-es! All our

bi - le ka - o - fe - la. Ha - le - lu - ya! Pe - lo tsa
hearts are filled with glad - ness! Hal - le - lu - jah! We sing your

ro - na, di tha - bi - le ka - o - fe - la.
prais-es! All our hearts are filled with glad - ness!

Fine

Christ the Lord to us said: "I am
Je - sus says to us still: "All who

Text: South African traditional
Music: South African traditional; arranged by Anders Nyberg
Text and Music copyright © 1984 Utryck; admin. Walton Music Corp. Used by permission.

wine, I am bread, I am wine, I am
do the Lord's will, all who do the Lord's

D.C.

bread, give to all who thirst and hun - ger!"
will are my sis - ters and my broth - ers."

89 I was there to hear your borning cry

WATERLIFE 97.96D

1 I was there to hear your born - ing cry, I'll be
3 When you heard the won - der of the word, I was
5 In the mid - dle a - ges of your life, not too
7 I was there to hear your born - ing cry, I'll be

there when you are old. I re - joiced the day you
there to cheer you on, you were raised to praise the
old, no lon - ger young, I'll be there to guide you
there when you are old. I re - joiced the day you

were bap - tized, to see your life un - fold.
liv - ing Lord, to whom you now be - long.
through the night, com - plete what I've be - gun.
were bap - tized, to see your life un - fold.

2 I was there when you were but a child, with a
4 If you find some - one to share your time and you
6 When the eve - ning gent - ly clos - es in and you

faith to suit you well, in a blaze of light you
join your hearts as one, I'll be there to make your
shut your wea - ry eyes, I'll be there as I have

wan - dered off to find where de - mons dwell.
vers - es rhyme from dusk till ris - ing sun.
al - ways been with just one more sur - prise.

Text: John Ylvisaker, 1985
Music: John Ylvisaker, 1985
Text and Music copyright © 1985 John C. Ylvisaker

Lord, we bring to you our children 90

NETTLETON 87. 87D

1 Lord, we bring to you our chil-dren on this fes-tive, ho-ly
2 Now may we in hon-est wor-ship, in this glad and sa-cred

day; grant to them your ben-e - dic-tion; grant to us your help, we
hour, give our-selves in true com-mit-ment to your ser-vice and your

pray. Bless the chil-dren! Bless the par-ents! May they grow in Christ our
power; to the task of Chris-tian nur-ture: teach-ing, train-ing, lead-ing

Lord: joined in faith and lov-ing ser-vice, in his Spir - it and his Word.
still in the way of Christ-like liv-ing till life's pur-pose we ful - fill.

Text: Frank von Christierson
Copyright © 1976 The Hymn Society; admin. Hope Publishing Company, Carol Stream, IL 60188.
All rights reserved. Used by permission.
Music: American folk melody, J. Wyeth's *Repository of Sacred Music, Part Second,* 1813

91 Like a mother who has borne us

AUSTIN 87.87

1 Like a moth - er who has borne us, held us close in her de - light, fed us free - ly from her bod - y, God has called us in - to life.

2 Like a fa - ther who has taught us, grasped our hand and been our guide, lift - ed us and healed our sor - rows, God has walked with us in life.

3 Though as chil - dren we have wan - dered, placed our trust in pow'r and might, left be - hind our broth-ers, sis - ters, God still calls us in - to life.

4 When we of - fer food and com - fort, grasp our neigh - bor's hand in love, tread the path of peace and jus - tice, God still walks with us in life.

Text: Daniel Bechtel, 1986
Copyright © 1986 Daniel Bechtel
Music: William P. Rowan, 1992
Copyright © 1993 Selah Publishing Co., Inc. www.selahpub.com All rights reserved. Used by permission.

Just as I am, without one plea   92

O WALY WALY LM

1 Just as I am, with-out one plea, but that thy
2 Just as I am, though tossed a - bout with many a
3 Just as I am, thou wilt re - ceive, wilt wel-come,
4 Just as I am, thy love un - known hath bro - ken

blood was shed for me, and that thou bid'st me come to
con - flict many a doubt, fight-ings and fears with - in, with -
par - don, cleanse, re - lieve, be - cause thy prom - ise I be -
ev - 'ry bar - rier down. Now to be thine, yea, thine a -

thee,
out,   O Lamb of God, I come, I come.
lieve,
lone,

Text: Charlotte Elliot, 1834, *Invalid's Hymn Book,* 1836
Music: English traditional; harmonized by James E. Clemens, 2004
        Harmonization copyright © 2004 James E. Clemens

93 Wehrlos und verlassen sehnt sich

RIFTED ROCK 87. 87 with refrain

1 Wehr - los und ver - las - sen sehnt sich oft mein
2 Drückt mich Kum - mer, Müh und Sor - gen, Mein - e
3 Sich - er bin ich und ge - bor - gen, denn bei
4 Kommt dann mein - e letz - te Stun - de, geh' ich

Herz nach stil - ler Ruh; doch Du dek - kest mit dem
Zu - flucht bist nur Du, ret - test mich aus al - len
Dir ist süs - se Ruh; mag es auch im Leb - en
ein zur ew'- gen Ruh; und Du deckst mit Dein - en

Fit - tich Dein - er Lie - be sanft mich zu.
Ängst - en, tröst - est mich und deckst mich zu.
stürm - en, Herr, Dein Fit - tich deckt mich zu.
Flü - geln e - wig - lich dein Kind - lein zu.

Refrain

Un - ter Dein - em sanf - ten Fit - tich find' ich

Text: Carl Rohl
Music: W. Warren Bentley, *The Chautauqua Collection*, 1875

Frie - den, Trost und Ruh; denn Du schirm - est mich so

freund - lich, schütz-est mich und deckst mich zu.

1 When I'm lonely and defenseless
   my heart longs for rest and peace.
   Then you spread your wings of caring,
   with your love you cover me.

Refrain:
   Under your soft wings of mercy
   my soul rests and is renewed,
   for you shelter me with kindness,
   keep me covered, close to you.

2 When I'm pressed by grief and trouble,
   you alone can rescue me.
   Refuge from all fears and worries,
   you, my Comfort, cover me.
   Refrain

3 Confident and gently hidden,
   I find sweetest rest in you.
   Through the storms of life you hold me;
   Lord, your feathers cover me.
   Refrain

4 When I'm in life's final moments,
   I will not be left alone,
   for your loving wings will guard me,
   I, your child, will be at home.
   Refrain

Translation copyright © 1992, 2004 Jean Wiebe Janzen

94

Blest are they

Irregular

1 Blest are they, the poor in spir-it, theirs is the
2 Blest are they, the low-ly ones, they shall in-
3 Blest are they___ who show mer-cy, mer - cy

4 Blest are they___ who seek peace; they are the
5 Blest are you who suf-fer hate, all be-

king-dom of God. Blest are they,___
her-it the earth. Blest are they who
shall be theirs. Blest are they, the

chil-dren of God.___ Best___ are they who
cause of me. Re-joice and be glad,___

full___ of sor-row, they shall be con-soled.
hun-ger and thirst, they shall have their fill.
pure___ of heart, they shall see God!

suf-fer in faith, the glo-ry of God is theirs.
yours is the king-dom; shine for all to see.

Text: David Haas, based on Matthew 5:3-12
Music: David Haas; vocal arrangement by David Haas and Michael Joncas
     Text and Music copyright © 1985 GIA Publications, Inc.

95 I want to walk as a child of the light

HOUSTON 10 7. 10 8 with refrain

1 I want to walk as a child of the light.
2 I want to see___ the bright-ness of God.
3 I'm look-ing for___ the com-ing of Christ.

I want to fol - low Je - sus.
I want to look at Je - sus.
I want to be with Je - sus.

God set the stars to give light to the world. The
Clear Sun of Righ-teous-ness, shine on my path, and
When we have run___ with pa-tience the race, we

star of my life___ is Je - sus.
show me the way to the Fa - ther.
shall know the joy___ of Je - sus.

Text: Kathleen Thomerson
Music: Kathleen Thomerson
Copyright © 1970, 1975 Celebration

Refrain

In him there is no dark-ness at all. The

night and the day are both a - like. The

Lamb is the light of the cit - y of God.

Shine in my heart, Lord Je - sus.

96 I'm pressing on the upward way

HIGHER GROUND LM with refrain

1 I'm press-ing on the up-ward way, new heights I'm
2 My heart has no de-sire to stay where doubts a-
3 I want to live a-bove the world, tho' Sa-tan's
4 I want to scale the ut-most height, and catch a

gain - ing ev-'ry day; still pray-ing as I'm on-ward
rise and fears dis-may; tho' some may dwell where these a-
darts at me are hurled; for faith has caught the joy-ful
gleam of glo-ry bright; but still I pray till heav'n I've

bound, "Lord, plant my feet on high - er ground."
bound, my prayer, my aim is high - er ground.
sound, the song of saints on high - er ground.
found, "Lord, lead me on to high - er ground."

Refrain

Lord, lift me up and let me stand, by faith, on

Text: Johnson Oatman, Jr.
Music: Charles H. Gabriel, 1892

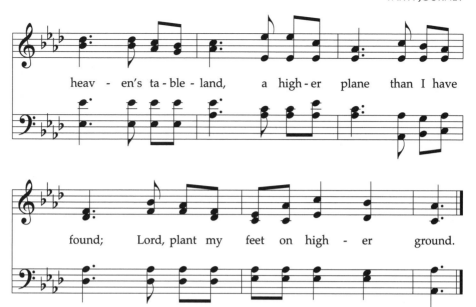

heav - en's ta - ble - land, a high - er plane than I have

found; Lord, plant my feet on high - er ground.

97 The Lord is my light

Irregular

1 The Lord is my light and my salvation, the
3 Wait on the Lord and be of good cour-age, O

Lord is my light and my salvation, the
wait on the Lord and be of good cour-age,

Lord is my light and my salvation;
wait on the Lord and be of good cour-age;

whom shall I fear?
he shall strength-en thine heart.

Refrain

Whom shall I fear, whom shall I fear?

The Lord is the strength of my life; whom shall I fear?

Fine

2 In the time of trou-ble, he shall hide me, O in the time of trou-ble, he shall hide me, in the time___ of trou-ble,

D.C.

he shall hide me; whom shall I fear?_____

98 All will be well

Irregular

Ostinato Refrain

All will be well, and all will be well, all

man - ner of things will be well.

Final

well, will be well, will be well.

Verses 1, 3, 5 *(Sung over hummed or played refrain)*

1 Our Lord___ said that all would be well, all
3 In all the doubts that shroud sim - ple truths, we
5 Our faith is firm and stands on the Word, the

D.C.

man - ner of things would be well.
pray for the wis - dom of God.
Word that en - dures for all time.

Text: Julian of Norwich, *The Revelation of Divine Love;* adapted by Steven C. Warner
Music: Steven C. Warner

Verses 2, 4, 6 *(Sung over hummed or played refrain)*

D.C.

2 With all the sad - ness wrought in this world,____ the
4 Give us the faith to trust in your love,____ when
6 And so we pray to trust in the hope that all

good shall____ al - ways pre - vail.
things are con - cealed from our view.
man - ner of things shall be well.

99 You walk along our shoreline

AURELIA 76. 76D

1 You walk a - long our shore-line where land meets un-known sea. We
2 You call us, Christ, to gath - er the peo - ple of the earth. We
3 We cast our net, O Je - sus; we cry the king-dom's name; we

hear your voice of pow - er, "Now come and fol - low me. And
can - not fish for on - ly those lives we think have worth. We
work for love and jus - tice; we learn to hope through pain. You

if you still will fol - low through storm and wave and shoal, then
spread your net of gos - pel a - cross the wa - ter's face, our
call us, Lord, to gath - er God's daugh - ters and God's sons, to

I will make you fish - ers but of the hu - man soul."
boat a com - mon shel - ter for all found by your grace.
let your judg-ment heal us so that all may be one.

Text: Sylvia Dunstan
  Copyright © 1991 GIA Publications, Inc.
Music: Samuel Sebastian Wesley, *Selection of Psalms and Hymns*, 1864

Here I am

Irregular with refrain

Refrain: Here I am, stand-ing right be-side you. Here I am; do not be a-fraid. Here I am, wait-ing like a lov-er. I am here; here I am. am. I am here; here I am.

1 Do not fear when the tempter calls you.
Do not fear even though you fall.
Do not fear, I have conquered evil.
Do not fear; never be afraid.
Refrain

2 I am here in the face of every child.
I am here in every warm embrace.
I am here with tenderness and mercy.
Here I am; I am here.
Refrain

3 I am here in the midst of every trial.
I am here in the face of despair.
I am here when pardoning your brother.
Here I am; I am here.
Refrain

Text: Tom Booth
Music: Tom Booth; arranged by Tom Booth, Ed Bolduc and Nancy Bolduc; accompaniment by Ed Bolduc
Text and Music copyright © 1996 Cristo Music. Published by Spiritandsong.com, 5536 NE Hassalo, Portland, OR 97213.
All rights reserved. Used with permission.

101 La ténèbre (Our darkness)

La té - nè - bre n'est point té - nè - bre de - vant
Our__ dark - ness is nev - er dark - ness in your

toi: la nuit com - me le jour est lu -
sight: the deep - est night is clear as the

miè - re.
day - light.

La té -
Our__

Text: Psalm 139:12
Music: Jacques Berthier
Copyright © 1991 Les Presses de Taizé (France). Used by permission of GIA Publications, Inc.

When from the darkness 102

COURTNEY 89. 89. 4

1 When from the dark - ness comes no light,
2 When in our con - fi - dence our fears
3 When in our love there is no care,

when from the weep-ing comes no laugh-ter; when in the day we
clutch at the heart and make us trem-ble; when in our joy we
and in our yearn-ing we are dull-ness; when what we know we

hope for night nor an - y com - fort com - ing
weep cold tears, and in our frank-ness we dis -
can - not dare, and we are noth - ing that is

af - ter: grant us your peace.
sem - ble: grant us your light.
ful - ness: grant us your truth.

Text: Brendan McLaughlin, *New Catholic Hymnal*
Music: Colin Mawby, *New Catholic Hymnal*
Text and Music copyright © 1971 Faber Music Limited, 38 Russell Square, London WC1

103 Why should I feel discouraged

SPARROW 76. 76. 76. 77 extended with refrain

1 Why should I feel dis-cour-aged, why should the shad-ows come, why should my heart be lone-ly, and long for heav'n and home; when Je - sus is my por-tion? My con-stant friend is he: his

2 "Let not your heart be trou-bled," his ten-der word I hear, and rest-ing on his good-ness, I lose my doubts and fears; though by the path he lead-eth, but one step I may see; his

3 When ev-er I am tempt-ed, when ev-er clouds a-rise, when songs give place to sigh-ing when hope with-in me dies, I draw the clos-er to him, from care he sets me free; his

Text: Civilla D. Martin
Music: Charles H. Gabriel

eye is on the spar - row, and I know he watch - es

me; his eye is on the spar - row, and I

Refrain

know he watch - es me. I sing be - cause I'm

hap - py, I sing be - cause I'm free; for his

eye is on the spar - row, and I know he watch - es me.

104 God moves in a mysterious way

UNION CM

1 God moves in a mys - te - rious way his
2 Deep in un - fath - om - a - ble mines of
3 Ye fear - ful saints, fresh cour - age take; the
4 Judge not the Lord by fee - ble sense, but
5 His pur - pos - es will ri - pen fast, un -
6 Blind un - be - lief is sure to err, and

1 won - ders to per - form; he plants his foot - steps
2 nev - er fail - ing skill, he treas - ures up his
3 clouds ye so much dread are big with mer - cy,
4 trust him for his grace; be - hind a frown - ing
5 fold - ing ev - ery hour; the bud may leave a
6 scan his work in vain; God is his own in -

1 in the sea, and rides up - on the storm.
2 vast de - signs, and works his sov - 'reign will.
3 and shall break in bless - ings on your head.
4 prov - i - dence he hides a smil - ing face.
5 bit - ter taste, but sweet will be the flower.
6 ter - pret - er, and he will make it plain.

Text: William Cowper, in John Newton's *Twenty-Six Letters on Religious Subjects*, 1774
Music: American folk melody; harmonized by Alice Parker
Harmonization copyright © 2000 Alice Parker

Don't be afraid

Irregular

Don't be a-fraid. My love is stron-ger,

my love is stron-ger than your fear.

Don't be a-fraid. My love is stron-ger and

I have prom-ised, prom-ised to be al - ways near.

Text: John L. Bell
Music: John L. Bell
    Text and Music copyright © 1995 WGRG The Iona Community (Scotland).
    Used by permission of GIA Publications, Inc., exclusive agent.

106 Just a closer walk with thee

CLOSER WALK Irregular

Refrain: Just a clos - er walk with thee, grant it,
1 I am weak but thou art strong: Je - sus,
2 Through this world of toil and snares, if I
3 When my fee - ble life is o'er, time for

Je - sus, is my plea; dai - ly walk-ing close to
keep me from all wrong; I'll be sat - is - fied as
fal - ter, Lord, who cares? Who with me my bur-den
me will be no more; guide me gent - ly, safe - ly

thee, let it be, dear___ Lord, let it be.
long as I walk, let me walk close to thee.
shares? None but thee, dear___ Lord, none but thee.
o'er to thy king - dom___ shore, to thy shore.

Text: North American traditional
Music: North American traditional

God remembers

GOD REMEMBERS 567. 56. 65. 8

1 God re-mem-bers pain: nail by nail, thorn by thorn,
2 God re-mem-bers joy: touch of love, taste of food,
3 God re-mem-bers us: all we were, all we are,

hun-ger, thirst, and mus-cles torn. Time may dull our griefs and
all our sens-es know is good. Love and life flow by and
lives with-in our Lov-er's care. Time may dull our minds and

heal our less-er wounds, but in e-ter-nal Love yes-ter-day is
pre-cious days are gone, but in e-ter-nal Love ev-'ry day is
death will take us all, but in e-ter-nal Love ev-'ry day is

now, and pain is in the heart of God.
now, and joy is in the heart of God.
now: our life is hid with Christ in God.

Text: Brian Wren, based on Colossians 3:3-4
Music: Marty Haugen

108 Give thanks for life

SINE NOMINE 10 10 10 with hallelujahs

Unison

1 Give thanks for life, the mea-sure of our days;
2 Give thanks for those who made their life a light
3 And for our own, our liv-ing and our dead,
4 Give thanks for hope, that like the wheat, the grain

mor - tal, we pass through beau - ty that de - cays, yet
caught from the Christ-flame, burst - ing through the night, who
thanks for the love by which our life is fed, a
ly - ing in dark - ness does its life re - tain in

sing to God our hope, our love, our praise:
touched the truth, who burned for what is right: hal -
love not changed by time or death or dread:
res - ur - rec - tion to grow green a - gain:

- le - lu - jah, hal - le - lu - jah!

There is more love somewhere 109

BIKO 66.96

There is more love* some - where. There is
more love some - where. I'm gon-na
keep on 'til I find it. There is
more love some - where.

*Additional verses: hope, peace, joy

Text: African-American hymn
Music: African-American hymn

110 Go, silent friend

LONDONDERRY AIR 11 10. 11 10

1 Go, si - lent friend, your life has found its end - ing;
2 Go, si - lent friend, for - give us if we grieved you;

to dust re - turns your wea - ry mor - tal frame.
safe now in heav - en, kind - ly say our name.

God, who be - fore birth called you in - to be - ing,
Your life has touched us, that is why we mourn you;

now calls you hence, his ac - cent still the same.
our lives with - out you can - not be the same.

Text: John L. Bell
    Copyright © 1996 WGRG The Iona Community (Scotland). Used by permission of GIA Publications, Inc., exclusive agent.
Music: Irish traditional; arranged by Alice Parker
    Arrangement copyright © 1968 Lawson-Gould Music Publishers, Inc.

Go, si - lent friend, your life in Christ is bur - ied;
Go, si - lent friend, we do not grudge you glo - ry;

for you he lived and died and rose a - gain.
sing, sing with joy deep prais - es to your Lord.

Close by his side your prom-ised place is wait - ing
You, who be - lieved that Christ would come back for you,

where, ful - ly known, you shall with God re - main.
now cel - e - brate that Je - sus keeps his word.

111 My latest sun is sinking fast

LAND OF BEULAH CM with refrain

1 My lat-est sun is sink-ing fast, my race is near-ly run; my
2 I know I'm near the ho - ly ranks of friends and kin-dred dear; I
3 I've al-most reached my heav'n-ly home, my spir-it loud-ly sings; thy
4 O bear my long - ing heart to him who bled and died for me; whose

stron-gest tri - als now are past, my tri-umph is be-gun.
hear the waves on Jor-dan's banks, the cross-ing must be near.
ho - ly ones, be-hold, they come! I hear the noise of wings.
blood now cleans-es from all sin, and gives me vic-to-ry.

Refrain

O come, an - gel band, come and a - round me stand; O

bear me a-way on your snow white wings to my im-mor-tal home. O

bear me a-way on your snow white wings to my im-mor-tal home.

Text: Jefferson Hascall, 1860
Music: William B. Bradbury, 1862; arranged by James E. Clemens, 2004
Arrangement copyright © 2004 James E. Clemens

I owe my Lord a morning song 112

NAFZIGER 86. 86

1 I owe my Lord a morn - ing song for
2 I owe my Lord a morn - ing song for
3 I owe my Lord a morn - ing song; the
4 I owe my Lord a morn - ing song. How

God has meant this day. Through
Je - sus rose at dawn; he
Spir - it gave me voice, nor
can I help but sing when

fears of night and hid - den light God
made death die and would not lie that
did she force my soul to praise but
God is all in all, and I am

moves and wills my way.
oth - ers might live on.
hon - ored me with choice.
one with ev - 'ry - thing.

Text: John L. Bell
Music: John L. Bell
Text and Music copyright © 2000 WGRG The Iona Community (Scotland).
Used by permission of G.I.A. Publications, Inc., exclusive agent.

113   For mornings bright

FOREVER PRAISED 88. 88. 55

1 For morn-ings bright with beau-ty's blaze, your
2 For gifts un-earned and yet re-ceived, for
*3 In you the sea-sons come and go, the
4 Let ev-'ry voice in har-mo-ny ac-

glo-ry span-ning all our days, for peace of
things un-seen and yet be-lieved, for trust in
o-ceans find their ebb and flow. In you the
claim the ho-ly Trin-i-ty. Let earth, in

dark-ness draw-ing on and hope of nev-er-end-ing dawn:
your un-fail-ing word, for joy in Je-sus Christ the Lord:
plan-ets spin their course, in you all be-ing finds its source.
splen-did sym-pho-ny, pro-claim your gen-tle maj-es-ty:

God of light, be praised, be for-ev-er praised!
God of grace, be praised, be for-ev-er praised!
God of time, be praised, be for-ev-er praised!
God of all, be praised, be for-ev-er praised!

*A seasonal stanza may be substituted:

Advent/Christmas
The night is dark, the winter long,
but God incarnate makes us strong,
who chooses here with us to dwell,
the Holy One, Emmanuel.
God in flesh, be praised,
be forever praised!

Easter
This is the day the Lord has made;
rejoice, no longer be afraid,
for like the amaryllis bloom
has Christ arisen from the tomb.
God of life, be praised,
be forever praised!

Lent
Oppressed by evil, crushed by sin,
we hear a still, small voice within:
"Arise, return, unveil your soul,
for Christ would touch and make you whole."
God in Christ, be praised,
be forever praised!

Text: Delores Dufner, OSB
Music: Randall Sensmeier, 2003

As morning breaks

114

Irregular with refrain

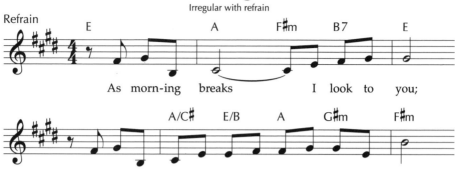

Refrain

As morn-ing breaks I look to you;

I look to you, O Lord, to be my strength this day,

To verses

as morn-ing breaks, as morn-ing breaks.

1 O God, you are my God, for you I long; for you my soul is thirsting.
My body pines for you like a dry, weary land without water.
So I gaze on you in your holy place to see your strength and your glory.

2 For your love is better than life, my lips will speak your praise.
So I will bless you all my life, in your name I will lift up my hands.
My soul shall be filled as with a banquet, my mouth shall praise you with joy.

3 On my bed I remember you. On you I muse through the night
for you have been my help; in the shadow of your wings I rejoice.
My soul clings to you; your right hand holds me fast.

Text: Psalm 63:2-3, 4-6, 7-9
Copyright © 1963 The Grail. GIA Publications, Inc., agent.
Refrain translation copyright © 1974 International Committee on English in the Liturgy, Inc. All rights reserved.
Music: Michael Joncas
Copyright © 1985 OCP Publications, 5536 NE Hassalo, Portland, OR 97213. All rights reserved. Used with permission.

Yonder come day

115

Irregular

Yon-der come day, day is a-break-in'. Yon-der come day,

oh my soul. Yon-der come day, day is a-

break-in'. Sun is a-ris-in' in my soul.

Text: Georgia Sea Islands traditional
Music: Georgia Sea Islands traditional

116 O joyous light of glory

JOYEUSE LUMIÈRE Irregular with refrain

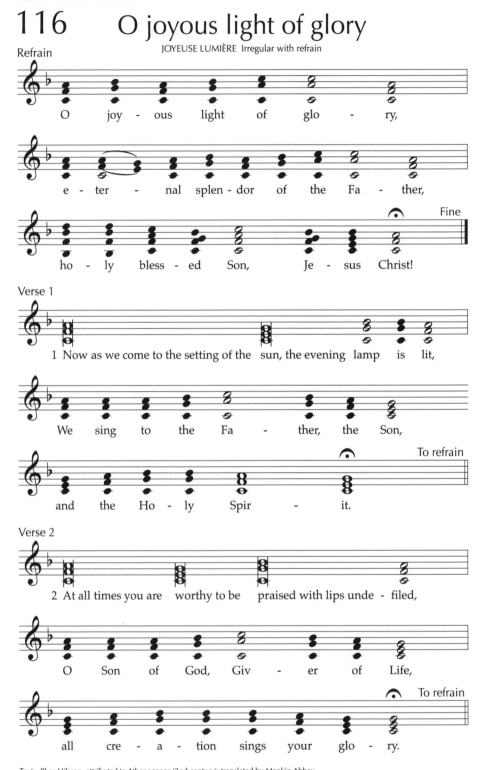

Refrain

O joy-ous light of glo-ry,
e-ter-nal splen-dor of the Fa-ther,
ho-ly bless-ed Son, Je-sus Christ!

Fine

Verse 1

1 Now as we come to the setting of the sun, the evening lamp is lit,
We sing to the Fa-ther, the Son,
and the Ho-ly Spir-it.

To refrain

Verse 2

2 At all times you are worthy to be praised with lips unde-filed,
O Son of God, Giv-er of Life,
all cre-a-tion sings your glo-ry.

To refrain

Text: *Phos Hilaron*, attributed to Athenogenes (2nd century); translated by Mepkin Abbey
Music: A. Gouzes
Copyright © 1983 Les Editions de l'Abbaye de Sylvanès, 12360 Sylvanès, France.

Verse 3

3 Let my prayer, O Lord, a - rise be - fore you like in-cense, and the rais - ing of my hands be as an eve - ning sac - ri - fice.

To refrain

Verse 4

4 Therefore in celebrating your glo - ry, we pro - claim the love of the Fa - ther, in the light of the Spir - it, burn - ing seal which makes you one!

To refrain

Refrain:
Joyeuse lumière,
Splendeur éternelle du Père,
saint et Bienheureux, Jésus Christ!

1 Venant au coucher du soleil,
Contemplant la lumière du soir,
Nous chantons le Père et le Fils,
Et le Saint Esprit de Dieu.
Refrain

2 Digne es Tu en tout temps d'être loué,
Par de saintes voix,
Fils de Dieu qui donnas la vie,
Et le monde Te glorifie.
Refrain

3 Que ma prière vers Toi, Seigneur,
S'élève comme l'encens,
Et mes mains devant Toi,
Comme l'offrande du soir.
Refrain

4 En celebrant ainsi ta gloire,
Nous chantons l'Amour du Père,
Dans la Lumière de l'Esprit,
Sceau brûlant qui vous unit.
Refrain

117

Night has fallen

DZUWA LAPITA 44. 44

1 Night has fall - en. Night has fall - en.

Gra - cious Spir - it, guard our sleep - ing.

2 Darkness now has come ...
3 See your children, Lord ...
4 We are with you, Lord ...
5 Keep us in your love ...
6 Soon we go to rest ...
7 Night has fallen ...

Text: attributed to Clement Scott; translated by Tom Colvin
Music: Malawian traditional; adapted by Tom Colvin; arranged by John L. Bell

Thy holy wings

BRED DINA VIDA VINGAR 76. 76D

1 Thy ho-ly wings, O Sav-ior, spread gent-ly o-ver me, and let me rest se-cure-ly through good and ill in thee. Oh, be my strength and por-tion, my rock and hid-ing place, and let my ev-'ry mo-ment be lived with-in thy grace.

2 Oh, let me nes-tle near thee, with-in thy down-y breast, where I will find sweet com-fort and peace with-in thy nest. Oh, close thy wings a-round me and keep me safe-ly there, for I am but a new-born and need thy ten-der care.

3 Oh, wash me in the wa-ters of No-ah's cleans-ing flood. Give me a will-ing spir-it, a heart both clean and good. Oh, take in-to thy keep-ing thy chil-dren great and small, and while we sweet-ly slum-ber, en-fold us one and all.

Text: Caroline V. Sandell Berg, stanzas 1 & 3; Gracia Grindal, stanza 2; stanzas 1 & 3 translated by Gracia Grindal
Copyright © 1993 Selah Publishing Co., Inc. www.selahpub.com All rights reserved. Used by permission.
Music: Swedish folk tune; arranged by Gracia Grindal and LaRhue Knatterud, alt.
Copyright © 1983 Gracia Grindal and LaRhue Knatterud

WORSHIP RESOURCES

GATHERING

119

Leader: Let all who are thirsty come;
People: **Let them drink of the water that has no price.**
Leader: Let all who are hungry come;
People: **Let them eat of the bread that has no cost.**
Leader: All without money, come, buy, and eat!
ALL: *Drink what is good, and delight in the Lord!*

120

Leader: Come, let us seek rest at the altar of God—
People: **Where even the infant can find comfort and protection;**
where even the weak can find justice and peace.
Leader: Blessed are those who dwell in God's presence—
People: **Where even the lily may grow in glory,**
where even the grass may be clothed with life.
ALL: *Blessed are those who trust in you, O Lord,*
our Home and our Provider!

121

God of love,
light a flame of love in our hearts to you,
a flame of love to our families and friends,
a flame of love to our neighbors,
a flame of love to our enemies.

Light a flame of love in our hearts to all,
from the lowliest thing that lives,
to the Name that is highest of all. AMEN

122

Source of all hope and holiness,
we gather this morning to be church.
Bless those who are absent, but not from our hearts.
Bless those who are distant, but not from your love.
Bless each of us here that we may
choose justice by your Spirit,
draw kindness from the well of your mercy,
and walk humbly in your path, O God. AMEN

123

Leader: You are home to the exile
touch to the frozen
daylight to the prisoner
authority to the silent

anger to the helpless
laughter to the weary
direction to the joyful:
come, our God, come.

ALL: *Come, our God, come.*

124

1: I will light a light
in the name of the Maker,
who lit the world
and breathed the breath of life for me.
(a candle is lit and placed centrally)

2: I will light a light
in the name of the Son,
who saved the world
and stretched out his hand to me.
(a candle is lit and placed centrally)

3: I will light a light
in the name of the Spirit,
who encompasses the world
and blesses my soul with yearning.
(a candle is lit and placed centrally)

ALL: *We will light three lights*
for the Trinity of love:
God above us,
God beside us,
God beneath us;
The Beginning,
The End,
The Everlasting One.

PRAISING/ADORING

125

Leader: God of all kindness,
we thank you for the many ways
your love enters our lives.

**People: You have filled our mouths with laughter
and our tongues with singing.**

Leader: Accept our sacrifice of song
in your church on earth,

**People: and grant us a part in the music
of your church in heaven;
through Jesus Christ our Lord.**

ALL: *AMEN*

126

Leader: Blessed are you, O God,
in whom nothing is wasted.
You salvage the remnant,
the scrap, the shred.
You bless what is left
from the consuming fire, the devouring flood,
the shearing wind, the shifting earth.
All that remains
returns to you
and is reborn from you.

ALL: *Blessed are you, O God,*
who brings life from the earth
and will return it to earth
once again.

127

My Lord and God,
the words of your Spirit are laden with delights.
As often as I hear them, my soul seems to absorb them.
They enter the heart of my body like the most delicious food,
bringing unbounded joy and unspeakable comfort.

After hearing your words, I remain both satisfied and hungry—
satisfied, for I desire nothing else;
but hungry, for I crave more of your words. AMEN

CONFESSING/RECONCILING

128

Leader: God of the weak and the wounded,
grant us your forgiveness.

People: **We have been heedless in our thoughts,**
cruel in our words,
shameful in our actions.
We are indifferent to a world made sad
by want and wastefulness;
we pass by on the other side
when we see our neighbor in need;
we wander from the way that leads to peace
in paths of our own pleasing.

ALL: *God of the weak and the wounded,*
grant us your forgiveness. AMEN

129

O God, before whose face
we are not made righteous
even by being right:
free us from the need
to justify ourselves
by our own anxious striving,
that we may be abandoned
to faith in you alone,
through Jesus Christ. AMEN

130

Reconciling God,
   who holds the brokenness of the world in a vast embrace,
restore us to your side,
   so we may offer healing and hope beyond our borders.
In the name of Jesus. AMEN

131

ALL: *Merciful God,*
       we have not loved you
       with our whole heart,
       nor our neighbors
       as ourselves.
       Forgive what we have been,
       accept us as we are,
       and guide what we shall be.

       (silence)

Leader: Listen to God's words of compassion:
         I taught you to walk and lifted you like an infant to my cheek.
         How can I give you up?
         I am the Holy One in your midst, and I will not come in wrath.

132

Leader: Lord Jesus Christ,
         we are your body
         not because we have chosen that name,
         but because you have given it to us.
         While we marvel at this great privilege,
         we also regret our failures.
ALL: *Lord, have mercy on us,*
         Christ, have mercy on us.
Leader: If, through false pride or selfish independence,
         we have said, "I am not part of the body..."
ALL: *Lord, have mercy on us,*
         Christ, have mercy on us.

(continued)

Leader: If, through superiority or lack of love,
we have said, "I don't need you..."

ALL: ***Lord, have mercy on us,***
Christ, have mercy on us.

Leader: If we have known that other parts of your body suffer,
and have refused to share their pain...

ALL: ***Lord, have mercy on us,***
Christ, have mercy on us.

Leader: If we have seen other parts of your body rejoice,
and have suspected or scorned their happiness...

ALL: ***Lord, have mercy on us,***
Christ, have mercy on us.

Leader: If, in place of you, the head of the body,
we have served our own theology, tradition, or prejudice,
and loved only those who loved or looked like us...

ALL: ***Lord, have mercy on us,***
Christ, have mercy on us.

(silence)

Leader: Let the body of Christ join hands and become one.

(All join hands)

> Lord Jesus, here is your body:
> it is frustrated and fallible;
> it is flawed and gullible;
> it is tired,
> but through you it can be made new.
> As your body,
> we wait on your word.

(silence, see below for alternative ending)

Jesus says: Come to me,
you who are weary and heavily burdened,
and I will give you rest.

Jesus says: In the world, you will have trouble.
But don't be afraid. I have overcome the world.

Jesus says: I love you.
I want you,
and I am with you...always.

(silence)

In the name of Christ our Lord,

ALL: ***AMEN***

(alternative ending based on John 13 and 15)

Jesus says: As the Father has loved me, so I have loved you.
Abide in my love.
This is my commandment,
that you love one another as I have loved you.
By this everyone will know that you are my disciples,
if you have love for one another.

(silence)

In the name of Christ our Lord.

ALL: ***AMEN***

AFFIRMING FAITH

133

Leader: O God, who called all life into being,
All: *the earth, sea and sky are yours.*
Leader: Your presence is all around us;
All: *every atom is full of your energy.*
Leader: Your Spirit enlivens all who walk the earth;
All: *with her we yearn for justice to be done,*
Leader: for creation to be freed from bondage,
All: *for the hungry to be fed,*
Leader: for captives to be released,
All: *for your kingdom of peace to come on earth! AMEN*

134

1: People who do not hold tightly to things are happy
because all of God's kingdom is theirs.
2: People who are gentle with the earth
will see it blossom forever.
1: People who can cry for all the world's suffering
will live to see happiness.
2: People who hunger and thirst for what is right
will finally have their fill.
1: People who really care
will find love wherever they go.
2: People who don't let the world get them down
will see God.
1: People who make peace happen
are God's children.
2: People who give up their own comfort so others can be helped
know what heaven is all about.
ALL: *Lord, let us be like these! AMEN*

135

Credo hispano

Creemos en Dios Padre todopoderoso,
creador de los cielos y de la tierra;
creador de los pueblos y las culturas;
creador de los idiomas y de las razas.

Creemos en Jesucristo, su Hijo, nuestro Señor,
Dios hecho carne en un ser humano para todos los humanos;
Dios hecho carne en un momento para todas las edades;
Dios hecho carne en una cultura para todas las culturas;
Dios hecho carne en amor y gracia para toda la creación.

Creemos en el Espíritu Santo,
por quien el Dios encarnado en Jesucristo
se hace presente en nuestro pueblo y nuestra cultura;
por quien el Dios creador de todo cuanto existe
(continued)

nos da poder para ser nuevas criaturas;
quien con sus infinitos dones, nos hace un solo pueblo:
el cuerpo de Jesucristo.

Creemos en la Iglesia,
que es universal porque es señal del reino venidero;
que es más fiel mientras más se viste de colores;
donde todos los colores pintan un mismo paisaje;
donde todos los idiomas cantan una misma alabanza.

Creemos en el reino venidero, día de la gran fiesta,
cuando todos los colores de la creación
se unirán en un arco iris de armonía;
cuando todos los pueblos de la tierra
se unirán en un banquete de alegría;
cuando todas las lenguas del universo
se unirán en un coro de alabanza.

Y porque creemos, nos comprometemos
a creer por los que no creen,
a amar por los que no aman,
a soñar por los que no sueñan,
hasta que lo que esperamos se torne realidad.

Hispanic creed

We believe in God, the Father Almighty,
Creator of the heavens and the earth,
Creator of all peoples and all cultures,
Creator of all tongues and races.

We believe in Jesus Christ, his Son, our Lord,
God made flesh in a person for all humanity,
God made flesh in an age for all ages,
God made flesh in one culture for all cultures,
God made flesh in love and grace for all creation.

We believe in the Holy Spirit
through whom God incarnate in Jesus Christ
makes his presence known in our peoples and our cultures;
through whom God, Creator of all that exists,
gives us power to become new creatures;
whose infinite gifts make us one people:
the Body of Christ.

We believe in the church universal
because it is a sign of God's reign,
whose faithfulness is shown in its many hues
where all the colors paint a single landscape,
where all tongues sing the same praise.

We believe in the reign of God—the day of the Great Fiesta
when all the colors of creation will form a harmonious rainbow,

when all peoples will join in joyful banquet,
when all tongues of the universe will sing the same song.

And because we believe, we commit ourselves:
to believe for those who do not believe,
to love for those who do not love,
to dream for those who do not dream,
until the day when hope becomes reality.

136

Leader:	Christ's food in our souls,
ALL:	*our food shared like his.*
Leader:	Christ's life in our hands,
ALL:	*our lives shaped by his.*
Leader:	Christ's love in our hearts,
ALL:	*our love warmed through his.*
Leader:	Christ's peace on our path,
ALL:	*our path following his.*

PRAYING

137

O Holy One,
we hear and say so many words,
yet yours is the word we need.
Speak now,
and help us listen;
and, if what we hear is silence,
let it quiet us,
let it disturb us,
let it touch our need,
let it break our pride,
let it shrink our certainties,
let it enlarge our wonder. AMEN

138

Leader:	Divine Teacher,
	may your word be
	a lamp for our feet
	and a light for our path.
People:	**As children of the light,**
	may we walk in the sure ways
	of your sacred teaching
	all the days of our life.
ALL:	*To you be glory for ever and ever. AMEN*

139

Holy God,
whose name is not honored
where the needy are not served,
and the powerless are treated with contempt:
may we embrace our neighbor
with the same tenderness
that we ourselves require;
so your justice may be fulfilled in love,
through Jesus Christ. AMEN

140

Leader:	To you, Creator of nature and humanity, of truth and beauty, I pray:
1:	Hear my voice, for it is the voice of the victims of all wars and violence among individuals and nations.
2:	Hear my voice, for it is the voice of all children who suffer and who will suffer when people put their faith in weapons and war.
3:	Hear my voice when I beg you to instill into the hearts of all human beings the vision of peace, the strength of justice, and the joy of fellowship.
4:	Hear my voice, for I speak for the multitudes in every country and in every period of history who do not want war and are ready to walk the road of peace.
People:	**Hear my voice and grant insight and strength so that we may always respond to hatred with love, to injustice with total dedication to justice, to need with the sharing of self, to war with peace.**
ALL:	*O God, hear my voice, and grant to the world your everlasting peace. AMEN*

141

Creating God,
for those who are wise
to the ways of your earth:
thank you.

For those who listen
to the language
of tree, rock,
river, earth,
ocean, stars,
creatures, sky:
praise.

Teach us
the vocabulary
to convey our care,
the words to tell the earth
we hear her crying for peace,
the syllables of solace

for all we have lost,
the gestures of healing
for all we have harmed. AMEN

142

Leader: God of all nations,
your love is without limit and without end.
Enlarge our vision of your redeeming purpose for all people.
By the example of your Son,
make us ready to serve the needs of the whole world.

ALL: *May neither pride of race nor hardness of heart*
make us despise any for whom Christ died
or injure any in whom Christ lives;
through the same Jesus Christ our Lord. AMEN

143

Holy God,
whose presence is known
in the structures we build,
and also in their collapse;
establish in us a community of hope,
not to contain your mystery,
but to be led beyond security
into your sacred space,
through Jesus Christ. AMEN

144

Most merciful God, we wait before you—
aware of our frailty,
aware of the fragility of our world and the peoples of earth.
We remember that we are dust
and to dust we will return.

Yet you are our Creator;
you are our Redeemer.
Hear our pleas;
hear our cries for mercy.

We wait before you
in the midst of a weeping and sinful world;
have mercy, O God, on our world—
on the places of violence,
on leaders who make war,
on people who hope for peace.
We pray for our world . . .
(free prayers of intercession)
Have mercy, O God *(followed by sung response, #47 Oh, Lord, have mercy)*.

(continued)

We wait before you
    in the midst of betrayal and broken relationships;
have mercy, O God, on our families and all we love—
    on children and parents who are alienated from each other,
    on husbands and wives who have forgotten how to love,
    on friends who wound each other,
    on churches struggling to live in peace.
We pray for our friends, families, colleagues, and fellow believers ...
    (free prayers)
Have mercy, O God *(sung response).*

We wait before you
    in the midst of sickness, grief, and death;
have mercy, O God, on all those in pain—
    those facing trials and temptations;
    those who are discouraged or bereft;
    those whose hearts are full of fear.
We pray for all in need of healing and comfort...
    (free prayers of intercession)
Have mercy, O God *(sung response).*

You are our merciful God;
your love never ends.
We rest in your care. In Jesus's name. AMEN

145

Leader: O God, we pray this day:
    for all who have a song they cannot sing,
    for all who have a burden they cannot bear,
    for all who live in chains they cannot break,
    for all who wander homeless and cannot return,
    for those who are sick and for those who tend them,
    for those who wait for loved ones and wait in vain,
    for those who live in hunger
        and for those who will not share their bread,
    for those who are misunderstood,
        and for those who misunderstand,
    for those who are captives and for those who are captors,
    for those whose words of love are locked within their hearts
    and for those who yearn to hear those words.

ALL: *Have mercy upon these, O God.*
    Have mercy upon us all. AMEN

146

Leader: Christ our Lord,
    long ago in Galilee
    many who were sick and suffering
    needed friends
    to bring them to your side.
    Confident of your goodness,

	we now bring to you
	those who need your healing touch.
ALL:	*Look on our faith,*
	even our little faith.
Leader:	We name before you
	those who are ill in body:
	whose illness is long,
	or painful,
	or difficult to cure;
	who suffer restless days
	and sleepless nights.
	(Here names may be said aloud.)
Leader:	Lord Jesus Christ, Lover of all,
ALL:	*Bring healing, bring peace.*
Leader:	We name before you
	those who are troubled in mind,
	distressed by the past,
	or dreading the future;
	those who are trapped
	and cast down by fear.
	(Here names may be said aloud.)
Leader:	Lord Jesus Christ, Lover of all,
ALL:	*Bring healing, bring peace.*
Leader:	We name before you
	those for whom light
	has been turned to darkness:
	by the death of a loved one;
	the breaking of a friendship;
	the fading of hope.
	(Here names may be said aloud.)
Leader:	Lord Jesus Christ, Lover of all,
ALL:	*Bring healing, bring peace.*
Leader:	In silence we name before you
	those whose names
	we may not say aloud.
	(Here silence is kept.)
Leader:	Lord Jesus Christ, Lover of all,
ALL:	*Bring healing, bring peace.*
Leader:	Loving God,
	the care of every soul
	is in your hands,
	the cure of every sickness
	comes from you.
	We do not know
	your will for us.
	If by our lives
	your grace may be made known,
	then in us, through us,
	or even in spite of us,
	your kingdom come,
	your will be done. AMEN

OFFERING

147

God of extravagant mercy,
  with hands outstretched you have poured out
  wonder and pleasure and delight,
  goodness and beauty and bounty.
So take these offerings, we pray, as our protest against all
  that is evil and ugly and impoverished,
  trivial and wretched and tyrannical,
  in our world and in ourselves—
That we, too, may be poured out for the world. AMEN

148

Leader: God has shown us the meaning of generosity
People: in the rich diversity of creation,
  in the overflowing love of Jesus Christ,
  in the never-ending gift of the Holy Spirit.
Leader: God has abundantly blessed us and called us
People: to be a community that honors each other,
  to be servants to others with joy,
  to share our love and material possessions.
ALL: Let us rejoice in what we have been given
  and in what is ours to give.

149

Those born of God use eating, drinking, clothing and shelter
with thanksgiving
to support their own lives
and to the free service of their neighbor
according to the Word of the Lord.

150

O God, to those who have hunger, give bread,
and to those who have bread, give hunger for justice. AMEN

151

The bright sun shines unblinkingly.
Wind sweeps the land.
No rain.
Old people shake their heads.
Little children and women move to the food camps.
Already there are many thousands in camps.
We all pray for rain.

In the towns and cities people stand in line.
As sugar, cornmeal, flour, and oil decrease,
the hungry look increases.
Lean years are upon us.

Teach us to care, O God,
in the Muslim way,
which does not hoard nor store for the future,
but shares gladly regardless of how little. AMEN

152

1:      We clutch our tiny bits of faith in tight fists
            shoved firmly in our pockets.
2:      We clutch it suspiciously, so unwilling to let it go—
            we don't want to lose it.
3:      We clutch it fearing that once it is spent,
            we will be without hope,
            cast adrift, out of luck.

1:      Help us loosen our grip.
2:      Help us to pull our hands out of our pockets.
3:      Help us to uncurl fingers stiffened over time:

1:      to grow,
2:      to shimmer,
3:      to pulse,

All: *to explode into the air*
         like a thousand red birds. AMEN

WITNESSING

153

Blessed be the ones
    who dance
        in the corridors of death,
    who sing
        in the hallways of terror,
    who laugh
        in the prisons of fear,
    who shout
        across the silencing walls,
    who love
        beyond the borders of hatred,
    who live
        to welcome home freedom,
    who die
        never turning their heads,
    who return
        as the rising of hope.

154

Victorious God,
  who breaks the powers that strangle and bind us,
liberate your people
  so we may join hands to dismantle what divides and destroys us.
In the strong name of Jesus. AMEN

155

Suffering God,
  who bears the wounds of the world with the strength of love,
stand with us,
  that we may willingly carry Christ's compassion into the pain of the world.
In the name of the Wounded One. AMEN

156

Guardian of the seasons,
    keeper of every time,
    tune us so to your rhythms
    that we may know
    the occasion for stillness
    and the moment for action.
May we be so prepared
    so aware
    so awakened
    in our waiting
    that when you prompt us
    into motion,
    our hands may be your hands
    and our purposes
    your own. AMEN

SENDING

157

Go into the world doing what the Lord requires:
    living with kindness and justice,
    walking your path humbly with God.
Then you will find yourselves blessed.

Know that yours is the kingdom of heaven
    yours the strength and mercy of God,
    yours all the blessings
        given to God's beloved children.

158

Leader: From where we are
to where you need us,

ALL: *Jesus, now lead on.*

Leader: From the security of what we know
to the adventure of what you will reveal,

ALL: *Jesus, now lead on.*

Leader: To refashion the fabric of this world
until it resembles the shape of your kingdom,

ALL: *Jesus, now lead on.*

Leader: Because good things have been prepared
for those who love God,

ALL: *Jesus, now lead on.*

159

May the grace of Christ
that daily renews our lives,
and the love of God
that enables us to love all persons,
and the fellowship of the Holy Spirit
that unites us as one body,
make us keen to discern
and prompt to obey
the complete will of God
until we meet again, through Jesus Christ our Lord.

160

As water falls on dry tea leaves
and brings out their flavor,
so may your Spirit fall on us and renew us
so we may bring refreshment and joy to others.

161

May God who makes all things new
dwell among us
and give us life.

162

Go in peace,
and may the holy God surprise you,
Christ Jesus be your partner,
and the lively Spirit call your steps.

163

Go with the strength you have.
Go simply,
lightly,
gently,
in search of Love.
And the Spirit go with you.

164

Christ has no body now on earth but yours;
yours are the only hands with which Christ can do his work,
yours are the only feet with which Christ can go about the world,
yours are the only eyes through which Christ's compassion
can shine forth upon a troubled world.
Christ has no body on earth now but yours.

165

Leader: May God lift up each sagging shoulder
and strengthen every weakened knee;
People: **may God straighten the path for each tired foot**
and turn to peace every embattled heart;
Leader: may God so bless each merciful word
and magnify every faithful deed,
ALL: *that each root of bitterness can be pulled from the earth*
and the tree of life planted in its place.

BAPTISM

166

Leader: Come, family of God,
come join the celebration of new life!

Left: Come, mothers and fathers,
Right: come, sisters and brothers,
Left: come, grandparents, friends and neighbors,
Right: come, family of God!

Leader: God is about to do a new thing.
Be glad and rejoice in what God creates!
ALL: *We have come to witness a birth;*
we have come to welcome new members to the body of Christ.
Praise God, the Giver of new life!

167

Faithful God,
by water and the Spirit
you bring us from bondage to freedom,
from darkness to light,
from death to life.
Keep far from us the spirit of fear,
and grant us the courage
which you give to all who know your love.
By the power of the Spirit
make us true sons and daughters of your grace
and faithful witnesses to the glory of the gospel;
through Jesus Christ Our Lord. AMEN

168

Refreshing God,
    for every stream and spring
      that wells up grace from deep within your love,
I give my free and heartfelt thanks.
The day has come
    when I draw forth rejoicing
      the water of trust and comfort from deep within your wells.
May all people hear my thanks to you resound in song.
May I hear my own voice glad with laughter
    praise you for this amazing day of days—
for I who would be so lost, so lost,
    am saved. AMEN

LORD'S SUPPER

169

Leader: Come, let us celebrate the supper of the Lord.
ALL: *Let us make a huge loaf of bread*
      and let us bring abundant wine
      like at the wedding of Cana.
Women: Let the women not forget the salt.
Men: Let the men bring along the yeast.
ALL: *Let many guests come,*
      the lame, the blind, the crippled, the poor.
Leader: Come quickly. Let us follow the recipe of the Lord.
ALL: *All of us, let us knead the dough together with our hands.*
      Let us see with joy how the bread grows.
Leader: Because today we celebrate the meeting with the Lord.
      Today we renew our commitment to the Kingdom.
ALL: *Nobody will stay hungry.*

170

This is the Welcome Table of our Redeemer,
    and you are invited.
Make no excuses, saying you cannot attend;
    simply come,
      for around this table you will find your family.
Come not because you have to,
    but because you need to.

Come not to prove you are saved,
    but to seek the courage to follow wherever Christ leads.
Come not to speak but to listen,
    not to hear what's expected,
    but to be open to the ways the Spirit moves among you.
So be joyful, not somber,
    for this is the feast of the reign of God,
      where the broken are molded into a Beloved Community,
      and where the celebration over evil's defeat has already begun.

171

Leader: What do you bring to Christ's table?

**People: We bring bread,
made by many people's work,
from an unjust world
where some have plenty
and most go hungry.**

Leader: At this table all are fed,
and no one turned away.

People: Thanks be to God.

Leader: What do you bring to Christ's table?

**People: We bring wine,
made by many people's work,
from an unjust world
where some have leisure
and most struggle to survive.**

Leader: At this table all share the cup
of pain and celebration,
and no one is denied.

People: Thanks be to God.

Leader: These gifts shall be for us
the body and blood of Christ.

**People: Our witness against hunger,
our cry against injustice,
and our hope for a world
where God is fully known
and every child is fed.**

ALL: Thanks be to God.

172

Hospitable God,
  who opens a door through bread and wine,
may we see the place set for us
  so that, in turn, we may welcome others to your table.
In the name of Jesus. AMEN

173

God, Food of the poor,
Christ, our Bread,
give us a taste of the tender bread
from your creation's table:
bread newly taken from your heart's oven,
food that comforts and nourishes us.
A loaf of community that makes us human,
joined hand in hand, working and sharing.
A warm loaf that makes us a family;
sacrament of your body,
your wounded people. AMEN

174

That peace
will rise like bread
we can always hope.

That justice
will flow like wine
we can always hope.

That the table
will make strangers kin
we can always hope.
That our hope
will rise like bread
we can always pray.

175

The feast is ended; depart in peace.
The work of the world lies before us.
Accomplish justice, with grace.

PRAYERS FOR MORNING AND EVENING

176

Leader: Lord, this day is your gracious gift.
People: May we walk in the clear light of your grace.
Leader: Give us a heart that is pure in your sight,
that we may see you.
**People: May we love our neighbors as ourselves
and truly deal justly with them.**
Leader: O Lord, may your gracious eyes be upon us
day and night.
*ALL: Bless all our undertakings
to your honor. AMEN*

177

Leader: O God, you summon the day to dawn,
you teach the morning to waken the earth.
ALL: Great is your name; great is your love.
Leader: For you the valleys shall sing for joy,
the trees of the field shall clap their hands.
ALL: Great is your name; great is your love.
Leader: For you the monarchs of earth shall bow,
the poor and persecuted shall shout for joy.
ALL: Great is your name; great is your love.
Leader: Your love and mercy shall last forever,
fresh as the morning, sure as the sunrise.
ALL: Great is your name; great is your love.

178

Thanks be to you, O God,
    that I have risen this day
    to the rising of this life itself.
May it be a day of blessing,
    O God, of every gift,
    a day of new beginnings given.
Help me to avoid every sin
    and the source of every sin to forsake.
And as the mist scatters
    from the crest of the hills,
    may each ill haze clear
    from my soul, O God. AMEN

179

God in whom we delight,
  we give thanks for the fresh light of morning.
As we rested in your care
  through the shadows of night,
may we dwell in your peace
  through the hours of this day.
Guide us in our work and worship
  so that when evening comes,
  we may once more give you thanks and praise.
Through Jesus Christ our Lord. AMEN

180

Leader: God our Creator,
           by your mercy and might
           the world turns safely into darkness
           and returns again to light.
People: **We give into your hands**
           our unfinished tasks,
           our unsolved problems,
           and our unfulfilled hopes,
           knowing that only those things
           which you bless will prosper.
ALL: *To your love and protection*
           we commit one another
           and all for whom we have prayed;
           through Jesus Christ our Lord. AMEN

181

Lord of every time and place,
as evening falls
fill this night with your radiance.
May we sleep in peace and rise with joy
to welcome the light of a new day in your name.
We ask this through Christ our Lord. AMEN

182

Keep watch, dear Lord,
   with those who work, or watch,
   or weep this night,
   and give your angels charge
   over those who sleep.
Tend the sick, Lord Christ;
   give rest to the weary, bless the dying,
   soothe the suffering, pity the afflicted,
   shield the joyous;
   and all for your love's sake. AMEN

183

Lord,
   it is night.

The night is for the stillness.
   Let us be still in the presence of God.

It is night after a long day.
   What has been done has been done;
   what has not been done has not been done;
   let it be.

The night is dark.
   Let our fears of the darkness of the world
   and of our own lives rest in you.

The night is quiet.
   Let the quietness of your peace enfold us,
     all dear to us,
     and all who have no peace.

The night heralds the dawn.
   Let us look expectantly to a new day,
     new joys,
     new possibilities.

In your name we pray. AMEN

184

For those who walked with us,
this is a prayer.

For those who have gone ahead,
this is a blessing.

For those who touched and tended us,
who lingered with us while they lived,
this is a thanksgiving.

For those who journey still with us
in the shadows of awareness,
in the crevices of memory,
in the landscape of our dreams,
this is a benediction.

Index of Copyright Holders for Hymns

1. Text: © Lutheran World Foundation
Arr: © 1984 Utryck; Walton Music Corp., admin. Used by permission.
2. Text: Gracia Grindal © 1993 Selah Publishing Co., Inc. www.selahpub.com All rights reserved. Used by permission.
3. Text and Music: © WGRG, The Iona Community (Scotland). Used by permission of GIA Publications, Inc., exclusive agent
4. pub dom
5. Text and Music: © 1985 GIA Publications
6. Text and Music: © 1990, 1996 General Board of Global Ministries, GBGMusik, 475 Riverside Drive, New York, NY 10115. All rights reserved. Used by permission.
7. Text and Music: © 1994, World Library Publications, 3708 River Rd., Suite 400, Franklin Park, IL 60131. www.wlpmusic.com All rights reserved. Used by permission.
8. Trans: © 1993 The Pilgrim Press. Used by permission.
9. Text and Music: © 1998 Vineyard Songs (UK/EIRE); admin. in North America by Music Services o/b/o Vineyard Music Global Inc. (PRS)
10. Text: © John Richards
11. Text and Music: © 1994 Earthsongs, 220 NW 29th Street, Corvallis, OR 97330, (541) 758-5760, www.earthsongsmus.com
12. Arr: © James E. Clemens (acc. Packet only)
13. Text and Music copyright © 1989 GIA Publications, Inc.
14. Text and Music: © Les Petites Soeurs de Jésus and L'Arche Community, Via Acque Salvie, 2 Tre Fontaine, Roma, Italy I-00142
Trans: © 1970 Stephen Somerville
15. Arr: © 1990 Wil WGRG, The Iona Community (Scotland). Used by permission of GIA Publications, Inc., exclusive agent.
16. Text: © 1987 WGRG, The Iona Community (Scotland). Used by permission of GIA Publications, Inc., exclusive agent.
17. Arr: © 1990 WGRG The Iona Community (Scotland). Used by permission of GIA Publications, Inc., exclusive agent.
18. Text and Music: © 1981 Sound III
Arr: © 2000, GIA Publications, Inc.
19. Text and Arr: © 1998 WGRG, The Iona Community (Scotland). Used by permission of GIA Publications, Inc., exclusive agent.
21. Text and Music: © 2001 WGRG The Iona Community (Scotland). Used by permission of GIA Publications, Inc., exclusive agent.
23. Text: © 1993 Delores Dufner. Published by OCP Publications, 5536 NE Hassalo, Portland, OR 97213. All rights reserved. Used with permission. Harm: © 1975 GIA Publications, Inc.
24. Text and Music: © 2003 Doug Krehbiel and Jude Krehbiel
25. Text and Music: © 1981 Peter W. A. Davison
Arr: © 1981 George Black
26. Text: © Oxford University Press. Used by permission. All rights reserved.
27. Text: © 1996 Hope Publishing Company, Carol Stream, IL 60188. All rights reserved. Used by permission.

Music: © 2001, GIA Publications, Inc.
28. Text and Music: © 2001 by Arlyn Friesen Epp. All rights reserved. Used by permission.
29. Text and Music: © 1992 GIA Publications, Inc.
30. Text: Copyright © 1995, WGRG The Iona Community (Scotland). Used by permission of GIA Publications, Inc., exclusive agent. Harm: © 2001 James E. Clemens
31. Arr: © 1990 WGRG The Iona Community (Scotland). Used by permission of GIA Publications, Inc., exclusive agent.
32. Arr: © 1991 WGRG The Iona Community (Scotland). Used by permission of GIA Publications, Inc., exclusive agent.
33. Text and Music: © 1995 WGRG The Iona Community (Scotland). Used by permission of GIA Publications, Inc., exclusive agent.
34. Text: © 1987 The Hymn Society, admin. Hope Publishing Company, Carol Stream, IL 60188. All rights reserved. Used by permission.
35. Music: © 2001 James E. Clemens
36. Text and Music: © 1993, World Library Publications. All rights reserved. Used by permission.
37. Text and Music: © Pablo Sosa
38. Text: © 1994 Susan Palo Cherwien, admin. Augsburg Fortress
Music: © 1997 Augsburg Fortress. Used by permission.
39. Trans: © 1975, 1986, GIA Publications, Inc.
40. Text: © 1983, 1998 admin. GIA Publications, Inc.
41. Arr: © GIA Publications, Inc.
42. Trans: © Makumira University College, Tanzania
Arr: © Austin C. Lovelace.
45. Arr: © 1978 Lawson-Gould Music Publishers, Inc.
47. Arr: © 2000, GIA Publications, Inc.
49. Text and Music: © 1993 GIA Publications, Inc. Refrain trans: © 1969 ICEL
50. Text and Music: © 1991, 1992 Jaime Cortez. Published by OCP Publications, 5536 NE Hassalo, Portland, OR 97213. All rights reserved. Used with permission.
52. Text and Music: © 1971, 2004 Gerald Derstine.
53. Text and Music: © 1962 Elena G. Macquiso
Trans: © 1964 Christian Conference of Asia. All rights reserved.
Arr: © 1980 World Council of Churches
54. Text and Music: ©1993 Bernadette Farrell. Published by OCP Publications, 5536 NE Hassalo, Portland, OR 97213. All rights reserved. Used with permission.
55. Music: © 1990 The Iona Community/Wild Goose Publications (Scotland). Used by permission of GIA Publications, Inc., exclusive agent.
56. Words and Music: © 1967, 1975, 1980 Franciscan Communications.
Arr: © 1968 OCP Publications, 5536 NE Hassalo, Portland, OR 97213. All rights reserved. Used with permission.
57. Text and Music: © 1991 John C. Ylvisaker.
58. Text and Music: © 1994, World Library Publications, 3708 River Rd., Suite 400, Franklin Park, IL 60131. All rights reserved. Used by permission.

Addresses of Copyright Holders for Hymns

Abingdon Press, The United Methodist Publishing House, 201 Eighth Avenue South, P.O. Box 801, Nashville, TN 37202-0801
www.abingdonpress.com

The Anglican Church in Aotearoa, New Zealand and Polynesia, General Synod Office, P.O. Box 885, Hastings, NZ

Augsburg Fortress, P.O. Box 1209, Minneapolis, MN 55440-1209, 800-426-0115
www.augsburgfortress.org

Church of Scotland, Panel on Worship, 121 George Street, Edinburgh EH2 4YN, Scotland, UK, 131-225-5722

James E. Clemens, 10605 Grapevine Lane, Dayton, VA 22821, 540-867-0155 www.jeclemens.com

The Community of Celebration, P.O. Box 309, Aliquippa, PA 15001, 724-375-1510
www.communityofcelebration.com

(Rev. Canon) Peter W. A. Davison, 1902-21st Avenue, Vernon, BC V1T 7B9

Earthsongs, 220 NW 29th Street, Corvallis, OR 97330, 541-758-5760, www.earthsongsmus.com

Arlyn Friesen Epp, Mennonite Church Canada, 600 Shaftesbury Blvd., Winnipeg, MB R3P 0M4, 204-888-6781

Faber Music Limited, 3 Queen Square, London WC1N 3AU, +44 (0)20-7833-7900 www.fabermusic.com

General Board of Global Ministries of the United Methodist Church, GBGMusik, 475 Riverside Drive, New York, NY 10115, 212-870-3783
www.gbgm-umc.org

Gerald Derstine, Slipstream Productions, P.O. Box 422, Snowmass, CO 81654, 970-963-4522.

GIA Publications, Inc., 7404 S. Mason Ave., Chicago, IL 60638, 800-GIA-1358 www.giamusic.com

Hal Leonard Corporation, P.O. Box 13819, Milwaukee, WI 53213, www.halleonard.com

Rev. Hope D. J. Harle-Mould, St. Peter's United Church of Christ, 1475 Orchard Park Road, West Seneca, NY 14224, 716-674-1233

Herald Press, 616 Walnut Ave., Scottdale, PA 15683, 724-887-8500 www.heraldpress.com

Hope Publishing Company, 380 South Main Place, Carol Stream, IL 60188, 800-323-1049
www.hopepublishing.com

Jean Wiebe Janzen, 5508 E. Lane, Fresno, CA 93727

Doug and Jude Krehbiel, 1125 N. Ash, Newton, KS 67114, 316-283-7351

Marlene Kropf, Associated Mennonite Biblical Seminary, 3003 Benham Ave., Elkhart, IN 46517
mkropf@ambs.edu

Lawson-Gould Music Publishers, Inc. 250 W. 57th St., Suite 1005, New York, NY 10107, U.S. Agent: Warner Brothers (EAM)

LCS Music Group, Inc. 6301 North O'Connor Road, Bldg. 1, Irving, TX 75039

Les Petites Soeurs Jésus, Via Acque Salvie, 2 Tre Fontaine, Roma, Italy I-00142

Liturgy Training Publications, 1800 N. Hermitage Ave., Chicago, IL 60622-1101, 773-486-8970
www.ltp.org

The Lutheran World Foundation, P.O. Box 2100, CH-1211 Geneva 2, Switzerland

Makumira University College, Box 55, Usa River, Tanzania (East Africa)

The Malaco Music Group, P.O. Box 9287, Jackson, MS 39286-9287, 601-982-4522

JD Martin, Slipstream Productions, P.O. Box 422, Snowmass, CO 81654

Morehouse Publishing, 4775 Linglestown Road, Harrisburg, PA 17112, 717-671-4500
www.morehousepublishing.com

Music Services, Inc., 1526 Otter Creek Rd., Nashville, TN 37215, (615)371-1320 www.musicservices.org

Oxford University Press, 198 Madison Avenue, New York, NY 10016-4314, 212-726-6000
www.oup.com/us

Alice Parker, 96 Middle Rd., Hawley, MA 01339
www.aliceparker.com

The Pilgrim Press, 700 Prospect Avenue, Cleveland, OH 44115, 216-736-3764 www.pilgrimpress.com

Phil Porter, 2273 Telegraph Ave., Oakland, CA 94612

Selah Publishing Co., Inc., 4143 Brownsville Rd., Suite 2, Pittsburgh, PA 15227, 412-886-1020
www.selahpub.com

Patricia J. Shelly, Bethel College, 300 East 27th St., North Newton, KS 67117 pshelly@bethelks.edu

Lois Siemens, Associated Mennonite Biblical Seminary, 3003 Benham Ave., Elkhart, IN 46517
lhsiemens@student.ambs.edu

The Society for Promoting Christian Knowledge (SPCK), 36 Causton Street, London SW1P 4ST, +44 (0)20-7592-3900 www.spck.org.uk

Stephen Somerville, Regina Mundi, 19309 Warden Ave., Queensville, ON L0G 1R0, 905-478-2733

Telephone Pole Music, Bob Franke, 106 Winona Street, Peabody, MA 01960-4637 www.bobfranke.com

Twenty-Third Publications, 185 Willow Street, Mystic, CT 06355

The United Church Press, 700 Prospect Avenue, Cleveland, OH 44115, 216-736-3764
www.unitedchurchpress.com

Walton Music Corp., 1909 White Plains Road, Chapel Hill, NC 27517, 919-929-1330

Westminster John Knox Press, 100 Witherspoon Street, Louisville, KY 40202-1396 www.wjkbooks.com

Wild Goose Publications, 4th Floor, Savoy House, 140 Sauchiehall Street, Glasgow G2 3DH, Scotland, +44 (0)141-332-6292 www.ionabooks.com

World Library Publications, 3708 River Rd., Suite 400, Franklin Park, IL 60131, 800-621-5197
www.wlpmusic.com

Rev. Dr. Brian A. Wren, Columbia Theological Seminary, 701 Columbia Drive, P.O. Box 520, Decatur, GA 30031

David Wright, Wheaton College, 501 College Avenue, Wheaton, IL 60187-5593, www.dwpoet.com

John C. Ylvisaker, P.O. Box 321, Waverly, IA 50677; 319-352-4396

Index of Copyright Holders for Worship Resources

FIRST LINE INDEX OF HYMNS

- Regular-face type indicates the original language of a hymn
- Italic first lines are given for translations of hymns when the original language also appears
- Upper case is used for titles of hymns that differ from the first line (often a traditional title) and in cases where English words may be used with a musical setting in which a language other than English is given.
- Upper case in brackets indicates first lines of stanzas found in the accompaniment packet
- Songs with an asterisk (*) indicate a keyboard/instrumental/solo arrangement in the Accompaniment Book.

TOPICAL INDEX OF WORSHIP RESOURCES